12/10/24

Wild Flowers

Mystery, Myth, Medicine and Images

George Proud

Published by Cartref Publications

www.georgeproud.co.uk

george@georgeproud.co.uk

A CIP catalogue record for this book is available from the British Library.

ISBN 978-0-9931589-0-2

Book layout and cover design by Clare Brayshaw

Prepared and printed by:

York Publishing Services Ltd
64 Hallfield Road
Layerthorpe
York YO31 7ZQ

Tel: 01904 431213

Website: www.yps-publishing.co.uk

DEDICATION

This book is dedicated to my wife, Janet, who has been such a help in our many outings when I have carried a camera and have been looking for wild flowers – and in the hope that many more outings also lie ahead.

CONTENTS

It is my great pleasure to welcome this fascinating book “Wild Flowers: Mystery, Myth, Medicine and Images” compiled by George Proud. I have a personal affinity with George who, like me, clearly not only loves plants and wild flowers, but values them for the impact they had on our forebears when no other treatments were available and for their mythology.

It is hoped that this book will re-kindle an interest in wild flowers as the reader learns about the diverse uses of plants in the treatment of many illnesses by the old herbalists, including TB, scurvy, the plague and even hernias and other fascinating tales such as why primrose plants were bad luck for poultry keepers and why knapweed flower buds were placed under the blouses of young and single ladies!

A walk in the countryside will become much more interesting when the book is used as many of the plants that are found in Northumberland, Durham and North Yorkshire (and the rest of the country) are described here and George has included some that are most common to our region such as the Spring Gentian and Birds Eye Primrose.

Jane Northumberland

12th Duchess of Northumberland

December 2014

ACKNOWLEDGEMENTS

My thanks are due to many people who have commented on the book in various ways, but always constructively, to assist in its completion. Plant identification is a problem sometimes: flowers do not always conform to what the books say. Kevin and Ros Charman have been especially useful in helping me out.

In the various talks I give on this subject people have contributed their own comments about folk-lore – they are just too numerous to include here, but I am grateful to them all. Some of what they told me is in the book.

In starting the book I had several tries at layout and format and Rev. Canon Alison White gave me great encouragement in telling me that what I had finally chosen was fine. This was a great boost, and she has been a great encourager at all times. Dr Stuart Scott, now retired from his work in English Literature at Newcastle University, deserves my thanks for the Kipling material, and much other encouragement.

York Publishing Services, YPS, has also been a source of great help. "Can I do it this way" is my usual question and this is usually responded to by "Yes". Duncan Beal – thank you. Clare Brayshaw deserves, and gets, a very special mention. She has shown patience and has been responsible for the final layout of the book – a not inconsiderable achievement for this type of book.

Whilst I have done quite a lot of the typing June Newton, my previous surgical secretary living in the village, has also assisted when the going got tough. Thank you, June.

My son Stuart has also helped. He is an accomplished photographer in his own right but when a particular grassy or rocky slope was beyond my ageing limbs he would take the picture of what I wanted. Again, many thanks.

My main thank you is for Janet, my wife. Not only has her camera come in useful on those occasions when a must-be-pictured flower is seen, she has tolerated my bursts of frustration with fortitude, has brought cups of coffee and tea when the flesh was becoming weaker than the Spirit, and even an occasional glass of spiritual support from Scotland! Not content with all of that she took on the proof-reading for me. I had not realised, in over 44 years of marriage, that she could be such a pedantic person when it came to grammar, punctuation and so on and to have such hawk-like eyes in spotting errors. I am so grateful to her for this.

George Proud

Riding Mill, November 2014

INTRODUCTION

Why did I compile this book?

It is hard for anyone to imagine what life was like before we had antibiotics, before we had vaccinations against diseases such as small-pox, polio, diphtheria, and so on, or before there was clean water available from the taps.

It was only in the twentieth century that these advances became available to everyone. I tend to think that the turning points came when drugs such as sulphonamides, bacteriostatic agents, became available for clinical use and antibiotics, bactericidal drugs, also became available in the 1940's.

Not only did these drugs come on to the scene but clean water was being introduced as a public health measure. In the later part of the eighteenth century chlorine was added to water to kill off the cholera germ and thus prevent outbreaks of cholera from occurring. However, it was not until the 1940's that water was becoming reasonably safe to drink. Today, in the twenty first century, the U.K. has some of the safest water anywhere in the world. Many countries still do not have safe drinking water and in those countries one of the commonest forms of death is diarrhoeal disease caused by dirty water.

Other developments have included developing or improving medical treatments and medical diagnosis. Even in the 1940's ether was probably the anaesthetic agent in widespread use. Gradually other, and much safer, drugs became available. On one or two occasions in my career, because of patients' drug intolerances, I have had to operate on those patients under ether anaesthesia: this was quite a frightening thing to do.

I could go on – but perhaps you are now beginning to think that our ancestors would need to be inventive in trying to treat disease. To begin with, they would need to be aware of the difficulties of diagnosis before investigations were possible such as reliable radiology or blood tests. They would need to work out in their own mind if they should take one of the many preparations provided by herbalists (and described at points in this book) to treat a hernia – or rupture as hernias were then known, or for any of a huge range of diseases. Nothing else was available – with the exception of amputations. The treatments used might have been based on experience, folk-lore, mythology, astrology and magic. Not a firm foundation for successful treatment – more a foundation for simple luck both good and bad!

Nor are we considering the herbal treatments in this book being applied only to people with whom we have no relationship at all. Any person now alive, and born in say the 1940's or 50's, would have grandparents who were in this era. That is very recent.

The problems of herbal treatments were beautifully described by Kipling in his poem "Our Fathers of Old" contained in the book "*Rewards and Fairies", pub 1910.* Kipling did have an interest in herbal treatments and was known to have a copy of Culpeper's herbal when still a schoolboy and it is possibly from that book he acquired his interest in astrology. A note on Culpeper is included in the brief histories of herbalists and also the bibliography.

“A Doctor of Medicine”-- Rewards and Fairies

Our Fathers of Old

Excellent herbs had our fathers of old--
  Excellent herbs to ease their pain--
Alexanders and Marigold,
  Eyebright, Orris, and Elecampane--
Basil, Rocket, Valerian, Rue,
  (Almost singing themselves they run)
Vervain, Dittany, Call-me-to-you--
  Cowslip, Melilot, Rose of the Sun.
  Anything green that grew out of the mould
  Was an excellent herb to our fathers of old.

Wonderful tales had our fathers of old,
  Wonderful tales of the herbs and the stars--
The Sun was Lord of the Marigold,
  Basil and Rocket belonged to Mars.
Pat as a sum in division it goes--
  (Every herb had a planet bespoke)--
Who but Venus should govern the Rose?
  Who but Jupiter own the Oak?
    Simply and gravely the facts are told
    In the wonderful books of our fathers of old.

Wonderful little, when all is said,
  Wonderful little our fathers knew.
Half their remedies cured you dead--
  Most of their teaching was quite untrue--
“Look at the stars when a patient is ill.
  (Dirt has nothing to do with disease),
Bleed and blister as much as you will,
  Blister and bleed him as oft as you please.”
    Whence enormous and manifold
    Errors were made by our fathers of old.

Yet when the sickness was sore in the land,
  And neither planets nor herbs assuaged,
They took their lives in their lancet-hand
  And, oh, what a wonderful war they waged!
Yes, when the crosses were chalked on the door--
  (Yes, when the terrible dead-cart rolled!)
Excellent courage our fathers bore--
  None too learned, but nobly bold
  Into the fight went our fathers of old.

If it be certain, as Galen says--
  And sage Hippocrates holds as much--
"That those afflicted by doubts and dismays
  Are mightily helped by a dead man's touch,"
Then, be good to us, stars above!
  Then, be good to us, herbs below!
We are afflicted by what we can prove,
  We are distracted by what we know.
    So-ah, so!
  Down from your heaven or up from your mould
  Send us the hearts of our Fathers of old!

Using this book

The great bulk of the book is given over to the plants. A very simple plant identification guide is included to assist you in finding the identity of a plant. A book of this nature cannot contain all that is known about every single plant – its size would be massive – or, in many volumes. Equally not every single plant you might see on a walk is included – but the great majority of the commoner plants are included, and a few rarer ones out of interest of the plant are also to be found. About 165 plants are described in detail and a further ninety or so are also included in the text.

What I have tried to do is ensure that the plants described in detail are representative of most of the genera of plants – and that should give you a lead in to finding a particular plant in a book which you saw on a walk somewhere should it not be in here.

You may consider the purchase of a plant identification book to be a worthwhile investment – guidance on this is included in the bibliography.

The appendix contains the common name for each plant described in its best known colloquial form. Plant classification, and its genus, are included in the descriptions for each plant – but the appendix is not artificially expanded to include all the Latin names as well.

I have also included in the photography section a note on photographing the wild flowers. This is a relatively simple task – people are so often put off trying to take close-up pictures because it is thought to be too difficult. Well, it is not too difficult and I hope you will give it a try.

The flowers are virtually all well known throughout the country, and not just the North of England where most of the photographs were taken. Rare plants have been included only if I think there is a special interest to them. For the most part shrubs are not included nor are trees.

Again, in the photography section, I include references to areas which I regard as special for plant photography.

Picking wild plant flowers is not, for the most part, a thing to do – mass pickings could damage next year's plants especially where annuals are concerned and which of necessity rely on being allowed to complete their life cycle and produce seeds. Some of the plants are protected and should not be picked. It is never a good idea to uproot a plant in the wild to transfer to your garden or for whatever purpose. I can hear many reading this to say that it is stupid advice if I see a Himalayan Balsam on a bank side, or a dandelion or similar plant growing, and I leave it – one fewer will make no difference and getting rid of something like Himalayan Balsam is doing something very useful. I am simply making a general comment.

A disclaimer: any herbal treatments described in this book are not recommendations that they can, or should, be used today. Undoubtedly some herbs are valuable in managing symptoms of disease but, as a surgeon, I must counsel caution if you are buying preparations over the counter, or from an internet source, unless you know what you are doing. The same applies to herbs picked in the country-side. Some herbs are potentially poisonous and require great care in use. Before embarking on herbal treatment for any new, or persistent, symptoms always be examined first by your doctor so that serious disease is not missed – and it is always wise to let your doctor know your intentions. Equally, when using herbs, my advice is to consult with someone experienced in herbal medicine if you wish to try treatments but lack experience.

How the book came into being

When preparing for A-levels very many years ago a practical assignment I did was to prepare a dried flower collection of a wide variety of plants, noting where they were found and making any comment I felt necessary about them. My early life had included many stays at my aunt's farm near Markington in North Yorkshire where I had learnt quite a bit about plants from her – more by osmosis in listening to her comments than by any active learning process.

However my career as a surgeon left little time to engage in what had become a hobby of photographing and documenting wild flowers. Mobile 'phones in my early career did not exist so, when "on call" I needed to be near a telephone and not walking the hills. Therefore it was not until retirement that the interest could be properly rekindled. By this time digital photographic methods were replacing film photography and I decided to start all over again.

There can be little doubt that plants have been an important part in the lives of our antecedents. I think it is important to remember this. Equally it is my impression that the younger members of the population have less interest in nature and especially wild flowers. A teacher acquaintance stated that in her class of eleven year olds, in a school in an affluent suburb in one of our towns, had no pupil who could name three wild flowers!

In a television series on Sacred Rivers, Simon Reeve the narrator and traveller described a place in the upper Ganges area thus: "*This place is so spiritual – I think it is because we are so connected with nature.*" A disconnect between humankind and the environment diminishes the sense of spirituality, something which people seem increasingly to seek in whatever way they may define spirituality.

It is perhaps easy to see why: towns that are increasingly crowded, with multi-storey apartments and few wild spaces, disconnect people from nature. A parish priest said to me that in his parish in a large town in the North of England the children in the parish had, for the most part, never seen a meadow pasture filled with flowers, had never seen a cow, or sheep – but they could describe the beaches in Turkey. Nature, and wild flowers are much less important than ever used to be the case. Perhaps it does not matter that people have no interest in their environment – yet with an increasing world-population the environment should be at the top of our lists of things to understand and care about.

Wild flowers are much less prominent in our fields and forests and verges than ever used to be the case. Better land drainage means damp-loving plants cannot survive; more specific herbicides help farmers eliminate such things as poppies and cornflower from their fields; neat, well shaven road-side verges – and path-side verges – have reduced significantly the number of flowers we might be able to see. This regular strimming out of wild flowers is in some ways irresponsible.

Wild-flower meadows are now a comparative rarity and may even be managed by Wild-life Trusts. A visit to an old-fashioned meadow containing a wide variety of wild flowers is a real energiser for me. Wild flowers are part of our heritage and we should encourage them to grow. I perceive this may be slowly beginning to happen.

Wild growing plants are well known in many countries of the world. People know and treasure their plants, and know what they might be used for as herbals. In Japan, on its west coast, the town of Toyama can be found. The University there has a modern medical faculty and patients are investigated by the very latest that medicine can offer and then their treatment is devised. For many that is Western medicine. However for a large number traditional medical treatment is sought. That is Oriental medicine or Kampo. Visiting the hospital's pharmacy and then being taken to the Kampo dispensary, it was clear that modern medical treatment is sitting comfortably with the Oriental treatments.

It was interesting to see the digitalis dried leaves in bottles being ready for dispensing. Liquorice was in bottles ready to be dispensed – and very many other preparations. Liquorice was prescribed in tablet form until relatively recently as a treatment for gastric ulcers or dyspepsia in the NHS. However, the University of Toyama was a World Health Organisation evaluation site for Oriental medicine and its department of Kampo is subjected to the same critical review as treatments given in conventional western medicine.

Researching the older herbal uses that plants were put to gives a wonderful overview of the types of disease which people suffered before the modern era of medicine. There were herbal medicines prescribed for all manner of diseases sometimes based on nothing more solid than a bit of astrology.

Such diseases were Scrofula, otherwise known as the King's Evil. This is a tuberculus infection of skin. Loose teeth and mouth ulcers feature regularly – these could be signs of gingival disease around the teeth caused by poor or absent dental hygiene, or could be scurvy which was really quite common. Another major problem seems to have been venereal disease: gonorrhoea was described as gonorrhoea, but the word syphilis was not used for the most part – instead, and in a hugely politically incorrect statement, it was known as the French Disease. Obstetric problems were seemingly common and tuberculosis beyond the skin variety was also a massive clinical problem. The plague was often referred to in the uses given for the herbs. These, and innumerable other diseases such as heart failure, epilepsy, jaundice and bile stones and kidney stones, regularly feature in the herbal uses we see described. What becomes very evident as one reads through all the preparations is that evidence based treatments just did not exist but –and especially so in Culpeper's descriptions – astrologically based treatments prevailed.

In the book is a glossary of terms and names, at least as far as I have been able to research them.

I have tried to identify the sources for some of the material I have used. Some of what is written down here is what I have learnt over the years, but where I can refer to a particular author I do so. All the sources are listed at the end in a bibliography. I have not given a reference number in the text nor do I give a page number to view the source of the quotation. What I have done is refer to (for example) Gerard, Culpeper and so on, so that the book can be consulted should you so wish.

I have also given a brief biographical note of the author of each book. This was fascinating to do.

In preparing a book of this nature it is inevitable that research is needed and in reviewing previously published descriptions of plants, and descriptions of their uses, one is relying on the author to be correct. Where possible I have tried always to corroborate what I have seen published regarding uses plants have been put to, and the names by which they might have been known. This has not always been possible and sometimes one has had to accept the single document rather than a group of articles giving similar attributes.

Where it has been especially important to try and review more than one article is in the situation where old physicians and herbalists have been quoted, especially Pliny and Dioscorides who lived in the 1st century A.D. I could find no translation of Pliny's works taken from the original by someone only interested in providing an English book of his writings.

In the case of Dioscorides an English translation is available but at a phenomenal price.

The herbalists and physicians of some centuries ago were usually classical scholars – so where I have felt that something was of interest in their quotations from the original writings I have referred to them – but please remember that they are uncorroborated quotations.

Natural rhythm of nature. The more I study plants, and their relationships with man, the more I become impressed with the rhythmicity one sees in nature. There is a natural cycle to plant life. In our environment in Northern Europe that rhythmicity is governed by the climate, just as it is in hotter climates. In the tropics some plants may complete their life cycle in a relatively short period of time and then re-grow. This is especially true for some grain crops – there may be several harvests of rice each year; there may be more than one growth of grass used to feed cattle and other animals each year.

In the U.K. we are accustomed to an annual cycle. After the period of rest in the winter plants re-emerge in the spring, grow, flower and set their seeds and then, in the autumn they go into a period of somnolence awaiting the return of the next season. Annual plants, of course, die off in the autumn – but by that time they will already have spread their seed by one means or another and in the spring new plants emerge. The spread of the seed may be scattering of the seeds, somewhat explosively, when the seed pod or capsule bursts. Others are spread on the wind and yet more are spread by birds. Some plants have developed a technique whereby their seed is spread by contact with animal fur – or human clothes. There are examples of all these in the flowers described. This annual cycle is ever present and can be anticipated. Some plants, when flowering, observe their own timetable – for example goat's beard flowers in the morning – at noon the flower heads close even in bright sunshine; the scarlet pimpernel will close its flowers in the mid-afternoon. Some flowers – dandelions for example – follow the sun when in flower. In the morning they face east and by evening will be facing west.

However, take another look at some plants – for example the dog daisy or sunflower. These plants, and many others, display a mathematical rhythmicity in their flower heads. The rhythmicity is found in a mathematical formula which I do not reprint here, but which in practice is simple. The formula was devised by Leonardo Pisano Bogollo, an Italian who lived from 1170 to 1250 – who was, and is, widely known by the name Fibonacci. This is translated as the "son of Bonacci". If one applies Fibonacci numbers to shapes one can make a beautiful spiral. Fibonacci numbers are sometimes described as *nature's numbering system* the **Fibonacci rule**.

The numbers constituting the Fibonacci rule are calculated as follows:

The first number in the sequence is 0 and the second 1. To get the third number the first two are added together – and one gets 1. Now to calculate the fourth number in the sequence one adds the previous two numbers – now 1 plus 1 – and the number 2 is obtained. The next number in the sequence is calculated by adding 1 and 2 together – it is 3. The next number in the sequence is 2 + 3 making 5, then 3 + 5 giving 8, and so on.

If one now looks at examples of wild flowers the Fibonacci numbers become most interesting. For example the number of outside ray petals in daisies is likely to be 21, 34 or even 55 according to the daisy – adjacent Fibonacci numbers. The disc florets are especially interesting for one can add up the number of spirals seen when the florets are studied in a counter clockwise or clockwise fashion. The number of spirals when measured in each direction are adjacent Fibonacci numbers. For example the sunflower may exhibit 89 spirals aligned in a counter clockwise fashion, and in the opposite direction the spirals will number 55 – both adjacent Fibonacci numbers. Smaller sunflower heads may show fewer florets or seeds – but again the numbers relating to the spiral arrangement are Fibonacci – eg: 55 counter clockwise and 34 clockwise – and the same will apply to larger seed heads or florets – 144 and 89 spirals.

Pine cones exhibit numbers in the spirals under this same sequencing of numbers – clockwise and counter clockwise spiral will have adjacent Fibonacci numbers and the same goes for Pineapples.

Elsewhere in the book you will find the sneezewort plant – in this plant the Fibonacci numbers also apply to the branches from the stem and next the number of leaves from the stems.

The Fibonacci numbers and spirals apply in various aspects of nature, but the **relevance** of Fibonacci numbers seems less easy to explain – why are all these relationships in numbers seen? Be that as it may the occurrence of Fibonacci numbers in nature is widely shown. A lovely account of the rule is given by Jamie Buchan in the small book *"As easy as Pi: stuff about numbers that isn't (just) maths". Pub: Michael O'Mara Books Ltd., London.* Available from Amazon at a knock down price. I found the whole book not only fascinating but understandable, and entertaining.

I hope that you enjoy my book – and that it incites a greater interest in wild flowers! Should there may be any errors that you spot do, please, let me know.

Some biographies

In the book a number of physicians, herbalists and others are referred to. This section provides a brief potted history of them.

Gaius Plinius Secundus AD 23 – 79. Plinius the second is better known as Pliny the elder in distinction to Pliny the Younger, the nephew of Pliny the Elder. Pliny had a number of attributes attaching to him. He was an army and naval commander as well as being a friend of the then Roman Emperor Vespasian. He was also a naturalist, an author and a philosopher, activities which he seemed to undertake in his spare time. As a result of his researches relating to natural phenomena he wrote an encyclopaedia which became a model for encyclopaedic writing. The encyclopaedia was Naturalis Historia – *Natural History*. He was also responsible for writing a treatise on the *History of the German Wars* but which is now a missing work. Pliny died in AD 79, probably from natural causes, when attempting to rescue a friend, by ship, at the time of the eruption of Mount Vesuvius which destroyed Pompeii: it is said that he may have died from the toxic fumes – but if he did die of that cause he was the only person on board who did so. However his influence on the development of the subject of the management of patients was quite considerable. I could not find any translation of Pliny's work, nor any reference to an English translation, so I have been unable to check references to quotations from Pliny by the later herbalists in the sixteenth and seventeenth centuries.

Pedanius Dioscorides. AD 40 – 90. He was a first century physician, botanist and pharmacologist. He had a special interest in herbal medicine, as was natural in those days – but he attempted to make the subject a little more objective by publishing a book on herbs and related medicinal products. This was "*De Materia Medica*", ("about medical material") a five volume work that was in use for the next 1500 years until Gerard and others came along and started to take the subject further. References are made sometimes in this book to Dioscorides. I have been unable to verify the references simply due to the fact I have not had access to an English translation (and my school-boy only Latin mostly long since forgotten). We tend to ridicule a little some of the old herbalists' recipes and materials used – but this was all they had in the management of disease or, at the very least, making the symptoms of disease more manageable by the sufferer. Dioscorides was a master of his "trade" and influenced patient management for 1500 years.

John Gerard (1545 – 1612 approximately). He was a botanist and herbalist and at his London home he had a large herbal garden. It was in 1597 that he published his main work, which became very widely read in the 17th Century, a heavily illustrated "*Herball*" or General Historie of Plantes, 1597. The book was 1,480 pages long. What Gerard had done was take some plants from his own garden and then he added these to the Herbal by Rembert Dodoen published in 1554. The wood-cuts for the illustrations were largely taken from Dodoen's own herbal and from other European publications. Gerard's *Herball* was corrected as far as possible and expanded to 1700 pages in the two decades after his death. He was a major influence on Herball treatment of disease – even sometimes declaring how much he had earned using a particular herbal treatment – and a plant genus of *Gerardia* is named after him. This genus is a root-parasitic plant including some of the snap-dragon group.

Nicholas Culpeper (1616 – 1654). Born in to a clergyman's family he went to Cambridge and studied Divinity. He became an expert in Latin, but left Cambridge before completing his studies and became apprenticed to an apothecary in London, who absconded after seven years with the money given to him for Culpeper's indenture. Culpeper decided to set up in practice in London as an apothecary in 1640 – and called himself "*Student in Physick and Astrologie*". He never qualified as a physician and his work as an apothecary was more as a pharmacist – but somewhat more extended than we know for modern pharmacists: many apothecaries worked in much the same way as General Practitioners today. He had brushes with the College of Physicians, especially after he translated into English the 1618 Pharmacopoeia in 1649, under the title *A Physical Directory*. He had done an unforgivable act by breaking the monopoly held by the Physicians. Culpeper was a prolific writer and published in 1651 the book entitled (abbreviated title given) *"An Astronomicall Judgement of Diseases"* in which he explained which planet caused a particular illness. It was the following year, 1652, when he published the book we know as Culpeper's Herbal. The original title was: *The English Physitian or an Astrologo-Physical Discourse of the vulgar herbs of this nation."* He said the agents he described could be *"Physically applied to the cure of all disorders incident to mankind"*. His approach to disease was clearly stated in the book on page v of the Epistle to the Reader (the introduction): first he would consider which planet caused the disease; then he would consider which part of the body was effected by the disease and then what tissue was affected by it; third, he would consider which planet afflicted the part of the body "governed" and finally used a herb which was of the planet opposite to the planet causing the disease. The planets were aligned as follows: Diseases of Jupiter could be treated by herbs of Mercury; diseases by Mars were countered by herbs under Venus and so on.

Culpeper had complete faith in his astrological methods. Culpeper died in 1654 from tuberculosis. He had eight children, but only one survived to adulthood.

John Pechey (1655 – 1716). Sometimes known as Peachey or Peche, he graduated MA from Oxford in 1678 and in 1684 was admitted a Licentiate at the Royal College of Physicians at the second hearing of his application. He practiced as an apothecary rather than as a physician. Perhaps the closest professional analogy today is pharmacist. (*NB A visit to the*

Apothecaries Hall in the City of London is a real treat). Pechey seemed to encounter trouble at the Physicians College and he had increasing fines imposed on him before he paid up in 1689 – the fine had by this stage reached £8. The size of this fine in today's money would have been pretty large. Finally, in 1689, he took the oaths of the Royal College of Physicians. He became a prolific author writing a five-volume series of books *Collections of Acute Diseases*, and then *A Collection of Chronic Diseases*. The first set of books included treatments for smallpox, plague (plague was rife in the country) and measles, and the second book treatments for hysteria, gout, and haematuria. These were published in 1692 and were quickly followed in 1692 by a collection of medicines. Many of his recipes were written out in full. Pechey's book *"The complete herbal of physical plants"* was published in the 1690's with an updated version appearing in 1707. It is from this second book that I take quotations in the text – along with one or two of his very complicated recipes. Pechey wrote other books including *"A treatise of the diseases of maids, Big-bellied women, Childbed women, and Widows".* Pechey produced some pills which were advertised at 1s 6d a box (seven and a half new pence). What they were, and how many were contained in a box – and what they might be used for, I could not ascertain. (NB Another John Pechey existed at this time – one John Peachi of Caen who sometimes called himself Pechey. He was a "Doctor of Physicke" in Gloucester who published a number of books but which are clearly now thought to have been attributable to someone else!).

The above biographies are based to some extent on referenced extracts from Wikipedia as well as consulting the books themselves as far as possible.

Lady Caroline Catherine Wilkinson (1822 – 1881). She was a lover of botany and although she had no botanical qualifications she wrote extensively on botany subjects. Her papers are included in a collection of papers from the Wilkinson archives at the Bodleian Museum in Oxford. The book (see bibliography) I have used is a very selective account of wild plants – *"Weeds and Wild flowers: their uses, legends, and literature".* It is a good read incorporating, as it does, Lady Wilkinson's own opinions which can be quite strongly expressed!

Geoffrey Grigson (1905 – 1985). He was born into the family of a clergyman in Cornwall. He became an Oxford graduate and in the 1930's he became known as a poet. He went on to be a book critic, and also did work with the BBC. He had a love of the country-side and botany, and his work *"The Englishman's Flora"* is a wonderful catalogue of wild flowers and plants and being distinguished by one of the most comprehensive of collections of the colloquial names given to plants in various localities in the country. It is largely unillustrated.

PLANT IDENTIFIER

The identifier is a simple attempt to enable plant identification of the plant described in the book. The precise plant identity may not be in here – but there is every likelihood that this identifier will at least guide you to the correct genus and then name of the plant you have found.

3 or 6 flower parts	2/4 petals	5 or more petals	Bell/funnel/tube	Pea/clover	Many petals or brush-like eg: asteraceae	Lipped/orchids	Umbels/spikes
Ramson's	Bittercress Cleavers Scurvy grass Bedstraw marsh Garlic mustard Holly Shepherd's purse Wild privet Woodruff	Strawberry barren Strawberry wild White stonecrop Rose – Burnet Sea/white/bladder Campions Chickweed Mouse-ear common Fairyflax Grass of Parnassus Periwhinkle Sea sandwort Spring sandwort Stitchworts Water lily Wood anemone Wood sorrel	Bindweed large Bindweed hedge Honeysuckle Comfrey	Clover white	Daisy Feverfew Oxeye daisy Sea mayweed Sneezewort	Dead nettle Eyebright Marsh helleborine Yellow rattle	Cotton grasses Cow parsley Ground elder Meadowsweet Pignut Sanicle (also pale pink) Sweet cicely Toothwort – (also lilac)
Bog asphodel Yellow iris Daffodil Mignonette	Crosswort Hedge mustard Lady's bedstraw Poppy Tormentil Golden saxifrage (lacks petals – is yellow green)	Agrimony Yellow stonecrop Buttercups Creeping cinquefoil Lady's mantle - 8 sepals Marsh marigold Mountain pansy Primrose Procumbent yellow sorrel Silverweed St John's wort Wood aven Celandine lesser	Cowslip Oxlip false	Bird's foot trefoil Greater bird's foot trefoil Dandelion Hop trefoil Kidney vetch Black medick Meadow vetchling Ribbed Melilot Common vetch	Cat's ear Colt's-foot Ragwort common Goat's beard Golden rod/Canadian ~ Groundsels Hawkweed Leopard's bane Nipplewort Thrift	Archangel dead Nettle Monkey flower Toadflax	Dog mercury Prickly sow thistle Smooth sow thistle Tansy Yarrow

3 or 6 flower parts	2/4 petals	5 or more petals	Bell/funnel/tube	Pea/clover	Many petals or brush-like eg: asteraceae	Lipped/orchids	Umbels/spikes
	Rose-bay willow herb Great willowherb Broad-leaved willow herb Pale willowherb	Bird's eye primrose Bloody crane's-bill Centaury common Rose dog/wild Stork's-bill common Cuckoo flower Dove's foot cranesbill Herb Robert Ragged Robin Lesser sea spurrey Water aven	Heather (ling) Bell heather Bindweed sea/ field Comfrey Foxglove Mallow common (pink/purple) Mallow Musk	Restharrow common	Butter bur	Common spotted orchid Wild thyme Hedge woundwort Marsh woundwort	Bistorts Wild angelica
	Honesty Speedwells	Autumn gentian Bittersweet Bugloss Butterwort common Violets Forget-me-nots Meadow cranesbill Wild pansy Periwinkle Purple loosestrife Purple milk vetch Spring gentian	Bluebells Viper's bugloss Comfrey Milkwort	Tufted vetch – pink/blue	Chicory Cornflower Burdock (blue/pink) Scabious Sea aster	Bugle Early purple orchid Chalk fragrant orchid Northern marsh orchid Self heal Ivy-leaved toadflax	Thistles
	Poppies	Campion red Scarlet pimpernel Seaside centaury (or dark pink) Valerian	Honeysuckle	Clover red	Knapweeds Mugwort (browny red)	Dead nettles Balsam Himalayan Blood drop emlets Pyramidal orchid	
Piri-piri bur							Broad-leaved dock Stinging nettle Ivy Lords and Ladies

THE PHOTOGRAPHY

Point and shoot. If you can handle a pocket camera's "shoot" button to take a picture then the great majority of point and shoot cameras should be able to produce good quality images of flowers. Most cameras have a macro or close up facility on the control menu: simply activate that and just see how close you can get with sharp results. Often the photographs are taken in the shade and if this is the case simply increase the ISO* rating – again there is usually a menu option to do this. Put it about the 800 mark. If necessary you can go to a higher figure but you may become aware of a little picture quality deterioration. Modern sensors generally cope with higher ISO ratings and, therefore, faster shutter speeds in the camera, thus reducing the impact of camera shake.

There is another reason you will need to have a relatively high ISO rating of say 640 to 800 is to taking photographs in breezy settings – an increased shutter speed should overcome any minor movement by the plant (or by yourself). Shooting wild flowers in a strong wind or a gale is usually a futile activity.

One other adjustment is important, and that is to set the image quality to the best setting – usually designated "fine" on the menu. This will allow greater magnification of the image for prints or for the screen image if you are projecting the pictures. Find this in the menu, press the button to activate "fine" and you are now ready to go out and take flower pictures. The rest can usually be left to the camera – and to experience by trying it out.

Compact system and single lens reflex cameras. In my own case I use a single lens reflex digital camera with a full size sensor (here the sensor in the camera is the same size as the old 35mm film cameras). I can adjust the ISO rating which I usually have at 640 or 800 and, when in darker areas, perhaps even 1000. The camera takes interchangeable lenses and the lens I use is the Sigma lens, with a 180mm focal length, and which allows close up images to life-size of small objects. The shutter speed is usually at least 1/500 sec. and often faster than this.

This set up allows me take some good images and the great majority of the pictures in the book were taken with this camera/lens set up. Many of the images are hand-held, but I also use a monopod to help steady the camera (a monopod also doubles up as a walking stick). For close ups a small bean bag, or something similar and light, will steady the camera. A tripod is useful, but adds significantly to weight.

Why a medium telephoto lens? With this lens the camera can be further from the image than a lens with shorter focal length. In addition the background to the flower is likely to be out of focus and blurred – this can be a great asset when taking pictures of wild flowers for usually the flowers are surrounded by many other plants of various shapes and sizes and blurring these allows the subject flower and plant to be more readily seen.

I have a small pocket camera which is very useful to carry around "just in case" when out on a walk. For all but the smallest of objects being photographed this camera serves me very well.

A few of the images in the book were taken by my wife, Janet, or by my son, Stuart. Janet uses a point and shoot camera and Stuart uses one also but usually uses his single lens reflex camera as I do.

I suspect that it will not be too long before cameras on telephones will be able to take pretty useful images of flowers.

The photographs

With only one exception all the pictures were taken in the wild and flowers were not picked to be photographed later. The one and only exception was the foxglove. The plant was pictured not in its natural environment but one growing wild in the small area of trees at the bottom of my garden was picked and one of the individual flowers was photographed to produce the "inset" image seen in the book. This image was taken by photographing the trumpet of a single flower at different levels from the open end to the innermost part at levels about two mm apart – about twenty four images were produced (the camera was on a screw-base attached to the tripod and was moved two mm forward for the next image, and again for the next until the flower was completely "imaged"). All the images were fed in to a software programme, known as Helicon Focus. The software is programmed to pick out the parts of each image in focus and simply stacks them one upon the other until the image is produced on the screen. Behind the flower image seen in the book are twenty two pictures. The time taken after loading the images to the programme was less than two minutes. The software is available to download from www.heliconsoft.com/. This is not the only soft-ware available – I have used this because it works for me and does not cost much to purchase.

ISO is short for International Organisation for Standardisation. It covers many areas of scientific measurements. For photography the ISO relates to the camera's sensitivity to light. The higher the ISO figure the more sensitive is the camera. Film "speeds" were measured in the same way – some were rated low ISO and some were rated high. Increasing the ISO allows the camera to be used in darker conditions. In plant photography raising the ISO rating will mean that the shutter speed increases. The raised ISO figure can also allow a smaller aperture. Both of these mechanisms will reduce the light going in to the sensor. What I do when photographing plants and flowers is to set the ISO – usually at 640 to 800 – but higher or lower if necessary. I then fix the shutter aperture, usually to about f8, then take the photograph with auto-focus switched on.

FAVOURITE PLACES FOR PHOTOGRAPHING WILD FLOWERS

Pretty much anywhere in the North-eastern areas of England and areas in Scotland. Chief among these are the Yorkshire Dales and North York Moors: upper Teesdale and especially the areas around Cow Green reservoir and in the hills of that area, and by the upper reaches of the Tees: upper Weardale in general but especially the high country and also Slitt Wood and Middlehope Burn to the north of Westgate in Weardale. In addition, in Northumberland, anywhere in either the North or South Tyne valleys and in the Cheviots, especially the Ingram valley. I leave what is arguably the best until last, and that is Holy Island. If you plan to visit Holy Island for any reason do check, and adhere to, the causeway safe crossing times (www.northumberlandlife.org/holy-island/).

However the great majority of the flowers described can be seen in most areas of the country!

BUTTERCUPS

Ranunculaceae

The plants: from the viewpoint of the family as a whole and the uses that buttercups have been put to, it is less repetitive to consider them all and then identify several which you may see on any country walk. In any case the buttercups have largely similar features with respect to the flowers. Most are perennial although the *corn buttercup* and the *hairy buttercup* are annuals as also are the *celery-leaved buttercup* and the *small-flowered-buttercup* which are annuals. These four are either less common in the northern parts of the U.K. or absent from them. The tallest buttercup can reach about fifty cm although some struggle to reach thirty cm

The flowers: are quite characteristic. There are five petals and, usually, five sepals. The petals are a bright yellow and shiny. Occasionally the number varies (for example one or two species may present with a rudimentary or absent petal in the cluster of five). The flowers vary in size with the common meadow buttercup having flowers up to two and a half cm whereas the relatively uncommon small-flowered variety has flowers about five mm across. The flower season varies from plant to plant although the buttercups usually start flowering in the early or mid-spring and one or two varieties carry on until well in the autumn. The spearworts, which look like buttercups but are much taller, flower from about June/July to the mid-autumn. They are not discussed any further under the buttercup heading.

The leaves: These vary, but most of the varieties are hairy to a greater or lesser extent. The leaves are best described as being rounded or oval in shape but with deep lobes – usually three but sometimes more. The lobes can be narrow.

Names, mythology, uses and folk-lore

Physicians and herbalists long ago recognised the plant's corrosive properties – and when discussing the buttercup they seem to do this lumping all the varieties together.

The flowers used to be called *crow-foot*, or *butter flowers*. The name buttercup is much more recent – probably from the mid eighteenth century according to Grigson.

The herbalist Gerard said they were *"very dangerous to be taken into the body, and therefore they require a very exquisite moderation.....not many taken alone......because they are of most violent force and therefore have the greater need of correction*".

Culpeper described the crowfoot as a *furious biting herb*. He gave the crowfoot a variety of colloquial names, including *frogsfoot, gold knobs, gold cups, King's knob, trail flowers* and *butter flowers* to name but a few. He described the herb in ointment form as being good for drawing blisters.

Pechey, quoting another herbalist, described the buttercup's value in curing headaches. Culpeper said that virgins in ancient times would use the powder from the plant to "furrow" (spread on) the bride's bed.

Various tales relate to the flowers. Many will remember the childhood game of identifying someone who liked butter by holding the flowers beneath the chin of someone – a yellow sheen on the skin identified the person as a butter lover. In Ireland the legend has it that buttercup flowers rubbed on the cow's udders improved the quality of the milk and increased its production. There is a touch of irony here for cows – as well as horses – tend to avoid buttercups in a field. Dried buttercups in hay are acceptable to the animals – the toxin, which is protoanemonin, is degraded by drying.

Buttercups which are most likely to be seen are the *spearworts, bulbous buttercups* which grow on dry ground, the *creeping buttercup*, which is a common invader of lawns, and the *meadow buttercup* which is shown here.

CELANDINE

Ranunculus ficaria: *Ranunculaceae*

The plant: The lesser celandine is common. It grows in early spring, particularly in grassy areas and, in my experience, it is most commonly seen in woodland areas which are only lightly shaded. It is a perennial and never grows to great height. The plant may reach about twenty cm but usually never much more than eight cms usually. The plant is very common, as already mentioned, and can be seen in many areas of Europe as one of the first flowers of spring.

The flowers: These are generally about 1.5cm in diameter and have between eight and twelve petals. The flowers only open in the sunshine and in spring time can be seen on almost any excursion into the countryside. Whilst many plants have the same number of sepals as petals, the celandine only has three sepals.

The leaves: The leaves are more or less heart shaped. They are characteristically glossy and a deep green colour.

Names, mythology, uses and folk-lore

Many of the names, unsurprisingly, contain the name butter or cheese: b*utterchops* and *cheesecakes* are such names.

Culpepper gives the plant a variety of uses, particularly in treating piles and haemorrhoids, and also kernels near the ears and throat called the King's Evil, and he writes quite coyly that he had another secret for his countrymen and women: *Pilewort* he said, as celandine was also known, made into an oil, ointment or plaster, readily cured both the piles or haemorrhoids, and the King's Evil. "*That poor people make much of it for these uses for this I cured my own daughter of the King's Evil, broke the sore, drew out a quarter of a pint of corruption, cured without any scar at all in one week's time*". In this regard one suspects that Culpepper was simply draining a skin abscess and not curing a tubercular abscess.

Allan and Hatfield confirm that the treatment of piles has been one of the most common uses of the plant. They said that extensions of this have been for the treatment of small lumps in women's breasts in the Scottish Highlands, for which purpose the roots were usually placed under the arms. They refer also to the use of the petals in some parts of the country for cleaning teeth.

A detailed description of the plant's use in the treatment of piles was by William Turner* around the time of Gerard or a little earlier, who used the name pilewort for the lesser celandine and he described it's use as follows: "*The later age uses the roots and grains for the piles, which being often bathed with the juice mixed with wine or with the sick man's urine, are drawn together and dried up and the pain quite taken away.*"

* Turner was an interesting man living between 1508 and 1568. He was born in Morpeth, Northumberland, the son of a tanner. He became a priest and worked as such until he was arrested but why I am uncertain. After his release he qualified in medicine in Italy and then practised back in England. He became Dean of Wells Cathedral and spent much time trying to unite the English and Reformed churches of Germany and Switzerland. This led to his suspension as a priest (for "non-conformity) and four years later he died. He was also an eminent ornithologist and published the first ever book devoted to birds in 1551 and then published a three-part herbal, which was a major advance in Botany. The lesser celandine was probably his favourite plant. After his death a lesser celandine was commissioned to be engraved on his memorial stone – but the engraver mixed up his plants and put on the greater celandine by mistake (Wikipedia).

MARSH MARIGOLD

Caltha palustris: *Ranunculaceae*

The plant: a plant of damp places, including damp meadows and woodland. Becoming much less common probably due to either herbicides or improved drainage of previously damp or marshy areas. This plant is in upper Teesdale – but it is now an uncommon sight. Grows to about twenty to twenty five cm. It is a perennial.

The flowers: are up to three cm in diameter. Although the first appearance is of five petals – that would be wrong for the petal like structures are sepals. They are bright yellow. Usually in flower between May and July depending on where they are growing.

The leaves: these are quite large, being about ten cm across on the mature plant. They are green and ivy shaped.

Names, mythology, uses and folk-lore

It has a huge range of names. Grigson devotes about one page to the variety of names given to it and these include *water Geordies, water gowan, water gollan, water buttercup* and so on. Some of my favourites include *bull's eyes, butter blebs and butter flower.* Inevitably with a plant of this shape and size of flowers the term button is applied to it with various descriptors being attached. However there are so many that space just does not permit a presentation of each.

The plant grows well in the North – and is probably one which grew before the ice age. It is a plant seen as far north as Iceland. I have seen it written that in parts of North America it is called cowslip (Grigson).

Culpeper describes the plant as being seen all summer long – and in the winter if it is mild. However its uses seem to be fairly unimportant – he devotes very little space to the plant which is unusual for any medically useful herb. It can be used externally in one form or another, and sometimes in possets and broths for comforting the heart. Applied as a plaster of the dried flowers, hog's grease, turpentine and rosin, and then applied to the breast over the heart will strengthen and succour the heart infinitely in fevers, whether pestilential or not. Overall very little has been made of the plant.

One modern herbal describes the plant being used in homoeopathy for blistering diseases and a variety of other conditions. Homoeopathy is a "treatment" to which I do not subscribe.

The plant is potentially toxic and this limits its use.

WOOD ANEMONE

Anemone nemorosa: *Ranunculaceae*

The plant: Wood Anemone is one of the buttercup family and grows to around twenty cm in height but can be a little taller. It can become quite prolific in its growing sites, forming a carpet of white flowers in moist and shady woodland. It is a perennial.

The flowers: The flowers are solitary on their stems and are generally one to 1.5cm in diameter. Their petals are white and lightly veined. The flowers often contain just five petals but can be up to ten – the example shown here has six.

The leaves: These are stalked and each leaf divides into three elements or lobes which themselves can appear to divide even further.

Names, mythology, uses and folk-lore

The flowers are very difficult to photograph for they nod in even the slightest breeze. These properties give the name *windflower* to the plant in many areas. A common name is an abbreviation of anemone – "*nemone*". Because of its early appearance, sometimes as early as "Candle Mass" (Candlemas*), February 2nd, it has been called *candle mass caps*, linking the flower to the purification of the Virgin Mary, but the plant has many names given to it and Grigson, once more, is a great source for these. The term *cuckoo* is often applied to the flower and it has links with snakes, particularly adders, and it is sometimes called *snakes and adders* or *snakes eyes* or *snake flowers*. Although the plant has virtually no aroma attaching to it, what smell there is is sometimes thought to be related to the fox and another name, therefore, has been *smell fox*. There are some associations between the plant and girls and their smocks, and with the anti-social activities of the cuckoo and also with snake associations.

When the flower is inspected it will be seen that there are many sepals which facilitate pollination by insects, and in the wild some of the flowers may be pale blue and even yellow.

Culpeper describes a number of different uses of the plant. Bathing in water derived as a decoction of the plant, Culpeper says, would cure leprosy. Using the leaves as snuff "*purges the head mightily*". He recommends that the root is chewed in the mouth for it procures much spitting and brings away many watery and phlegmatic humours and is therefore excellent for the lethargy.

Clearly Culpeper had some problems with physicians (qualified doctors of the time) for he wrote "*and when all is done, let physicians prate to what they please, all the pills in the dispensary purge not the head like to hot things held in the mouth.*"

He also said that an ointment derived from the plant and applied to the eyelids helped inflammation of the eyes, and the same ointment was useful in cleaning malignant and corroding ulcers. Allan and Hatfield, who have brought many of the old uses of plants into the modern era and discuss them as such, introduced the small section they have on the wood anemone as follows: "*too many misadventures with the toxic anemone nemorosa in village medicine appears to have largely eliminated it from the folk repertory.*"

The poisonous parts of the plants are known as **protoanemonin** which, according to an entry on Wikipedia, causes severe skin and gastrointestinal irritation, gives a bitter taste and a burning in the mouth and throat. Wood anemone, in common with some other ranunculaceae, causes mouth ulcers, nausea, vomiting, diarrhoea, and some individuals after taking it may vomit blood.

So it is a pretty nasty plant. Just enjoy watching it for it lightens up many a dull forest floor in late winter.

* The Purification of Mary is on the fortieth day after the birth of Christ (February 2nd) and is a ritual from the Law from Moses – the Mosaic Law – at this time the new mother presents herself for the ritual cleansing. It is the day when the infant is presented in to the Temple, having been circumcised on the eighth day after being born, and this Presentation is part of the ritual of cleansing of the mother (Luke 2:21-38 is the passage from the Bible which refers to this custom). The Old Testament gives, in Leviticus 12: 1-8, the Law on which this tradition is based.

CLEAVERS

Galium aparine: *Rubiaceae*

The plant: a very common plant and seen especially in hedges and undisturbed woodland areas. Only an annual it seems to be a quite rampant invader where-ever it appears. Everyone knows it for the plant sticks on virtually any clothing – and this applies especially to the fruits. It is difficult to estimate the size of the plants for they grow through vegetation – but they can be up to two m. long.

The flowers: tiny white flowers with four petals. Sometimes they might have a green tinge to them. They are no more than two mm across. The fruits are covered in hooks which attach very effectively to clothing and animal hair – and thus are readily disseminated. Seen throughout the summer.

The leaves: are covered in hairs – perhaps bristles might be a better description for those at the edges of the leaves are backward pointing thus facilitating the plants growth through vegetation.

Names, mythology, uses and folk-lore

There is a huge range of names described by Grigson and also on internet sites. Some of those I like include *Jack run the hedge, Lizzie run the hedge, tether grass, Robin run the dyke,* and *blood tongue.* This last name is described as coming from the observation that if the plant is rubbed across the tongue, it causes bleeding.

Another name is *goose grass* and this comes from the fact that the plant is eaten by geese and is fed to goslings. Some herbal uses have included using cleavers for piles, scurvy, ulcers and skin disease.

The name *cleavers* may come from the plant's physical characteristics for it cleaves the stem, leaves and fruit to the passer by.

COMMON MARSH BEDSTRAW

Galium palustre: *Rubiaceae*

The plant: grows in damp grassy places – the plant photographed was in a moor-side ditch in Upper Teesdale. It appears straggly, and looks delicate, but the stems are more robust than might appear at first.

The flowers: are tiny and do not exceed three mm or so across. They have the typical Galium pattern to them – they are white and have four petals arranged in a cruciform pattern. The plant flowers in mid-summer.

The leaves: arranged in whorls up the stem with about five or six slender leaves in each with bristles on the edges.

Names, mythology, uses and folk-lore

There is a scarcity of written information recorded about the plant. Allen and Hatfield record that it was used in the Northern Shetland Islands for dropsy – the plant was applied externally to swollen areas.

CROSSWORT

Cruciata laevipes: *Rubiaceae*

The plant: A remarkably common perennial grass-land plant in the North-east of England – but less common in the West and the North. It is a member of the bedstraw family of plants and this is shown especially by the flowers. It is hairy, as shown in the photograph, and the stems are square. This plant was photographed in a meadow maintained by the Wildlife Trust for Northumberland at Riding Mill, but it can be seen in many sites including roadside ditches and woodlands. Grows to about fifty cm in the most favourable circumstances – frequently much lower: on Holy Island and on Pennine roadsides they may only be ten to twenty cm high.

The flowers: are present in the early summer and arise in whorls from the stem: they are usually quite tightly packed. The flowers are tiny – about two or three mm. across – and the four petals are arranged in a cruciform fashion. They arise from the leaf axils at intervals up the stem. Some descriptions of the flowers say that they are 'frothy' – this is not how I would describe them.

The leaves: are most like an oval with a point. Arise at intervals up the stem in groups of four.

Names, mythology, uses, and folk-lore

There seems to be very little written about its herbal uses although Culpepper does come to the rescue. As with many of his plant recipes he says that a decoction of the plant in wine is good for ruptures. It is a vulnerary herb, (a herb used for treating wounds) and will also treat blocked breasts, getting phlegm off the chest and cleans wounds.

Sometimes known colloquially as *lady's bedstraw* (q.v) and also *maiden's hair* – but it seems to be a plant which excited little interest from the old herbalists.

LADY'S BEDSTRAW

Galium verum: *Rubiaceae*

The plant: seen in dry grassland and on sandy soil. This plant was growing in the sand-dune area of Holy island. It can grow to about thirty cm. The stems are square in cross section and the plant may smell of hay. The plant is common in most of the United Kingdom.

The flowers: appear between June and September and they are in dense clusters at the ends of stems. The individual flowers are not more than about two to three mm in diameter. Like all bedstraws the flowers are 4-petalled – and this is the only true yellow bedstraw. The seeds are black nutlets.

The leaves: Not seen here, are narrow and at the edges quite downy. They go black as the plant dries out.

Names, mythology, uses and folk-lore

Lady's bedstraw has acquired a number of names in folk-lore. Some of these include *Lady's golden bedstraw, Kee slip* (after cheese), *lady's tresses, rennet, robin run the hedge, straw bed, half smart,* and *Maid's hair* (from the time of Henry VIII). A French name has also clung to lady's bedstraw – *Petty Muggett* – from the French *petit muguet* or little dandy. In Scandinavia it was known as Frigg's grass: Frigg was a Norse goddess, and was the goddess of married women. Her husband was **Odin,** also a Norse god, and their son was **Baldr** (see *sea mayweed).* She helped women in childbirth. Scandinavians used the plant at this time in a woman's life and called it Frigg's grass.

There is a well described reference by Grigson to an association with the birth of Christ and this is associated with a number of other writers. Grigson gives a simple account of this telling the reader that *On a bedstraw of bracken and Galium verum lay the Virgin Mary. Bracken refused to recognise the child born – therefore it lost its flower, whereas the bedstraw welcomed the child Jesus and turned to a golden yellow.* Another legend states that it was the only plant in the stable not eaten by the donkey.

Grigson also refers to Chaucer writing about lady's bedstraw: *O perilous syr (sir) that in the bedstraw breedeth.* In Germany, however, the women of the Sudetenland used to put bedstraw in to their beds at the time of childbirth: it made the birth safer and protected the new mother from demons. German names for the flower include Marienbettstroh (the straw of Mary's bed) (–from Grigson).

The plant is quite aromatic and especially so in the warm damp evening – it smells of hay. In the past, the dried plants were used to stuff mattress as the coumarin scent of the plants acted as a flea killer. As one of its names suggest – rennet - it is used in cheese making to curdle the milk – and also to colour double Gloucester cheese (Wikipedia).

In the 17th century it was used as an ointment to refresh the traveller. Grigson also describes its use to wash the traveller's feet.

Although many uses and associations are described only one herbal use seems to have been described in the U.K. – it has been used to treat fits in dogs. There is an occasional reference to the treatment of human epilepsy – but the dog use seems better described. Lady Wilkinson writes that the flowers boiled in water, and the distillate taken, results in a very pleasant drink!

One of Holy Island's beaches

WOODRUFF

Galium odoratum: *Rubiaceae*

The plant: Where this plant is seen it is often commonly seen in the locality but you can travel far without seeing it. Like one of its stable mates, *ladies' bedstraw,* it has a sweet smell of hay especially when dried. Grows to about twenty to twenty five cm – in my experience usually shorter than longer. Seems to grow best in damp and, quite often, dark woodland. Is a perennial. It is a Galium – but is sometimes included as a member of the *Asperula* genus as Grigson does.

The flowers: small and white – about four mm across. Petals are four in number and arranged in cruciate fashion as with the other bedstraws. Give off a sweet smell – due to the presence of coumarin, an agent which is used in cosmetics (can be produced synthetically). Flowers seen in the early summer.

The leaves: there are usually between five and nine leaves arranged in a whorl at intervals up the stem – which is a characteristic of this genus. Are green and have a brush-like border to them.

Names, mythology, uses and folk-lore

Legend has it that in mediaeval times the plant was used as a church decoration on St Barnabas day (June 11th).

Medical uses are quoted in several places and Pechey describes its use in treating diseases of the liver including obstructions of the liver and gallbladder.

If the leaves/flowers are put in to wine the plant imparts a pleasant taste to the drink: this was especially a habit in Germany – called the *Maibowle (may-cup)*. Another German drink from Berlin is a beer which uses the plant – *Berliner Weisse (Berlin pale-ale)*.

The plant has also been used to flavour foods, confectionary and ice-cream but its use in this regard is now restricted due to its potential hepato-toxicity – coumarin is a benzo-pyrone. However the concentration in plants is small. Coumarin is very closely related – chemically – to the anticoagulant warfarin.

Allen and Hatfield record that the plant has been applied to cuts and scratches in parts of England from the 17th century right up to the early 20th century.

Other names include *sweet woodruff*, which is easy to understand why, and another which I can find no reason for – *wild baby's breath*.

WILD PRIVET

Ligustrum vulgare: *Oleaceae*

The plant: a shrub that is described as semi-evergreen. In warmer areas it is deciduous, but in colder climes sheds its leaves in the autumn. Can become very tall – up to eight to ten metres. It is a much branched structure and appears quite dense when found growing. This plant was found growing amongst other wild shrubs on Holy island. In the time of Queen Elizabeth 1st it was a common hedge-plant – but the Japanese plant, *ligustrum ovalifolium* is now the one commonly seen in British gardens. It grows mainly on calcareous soils.

The flowers: are clustered together in terminal spikes. Each flower is only a few mm across. The plant flowers in the earlier summer – May and June – but this plant was in full flower in July. The four petals are white – or creamy-white – and are quite strong smelling. The flowers give way to clusters of berries which are usually black. These are highly poisonous to humans – but birds, especially thrushes, seem to thrive on them.

The leaves: are an elongated oval in shape and are shiny.

Names, mythology, uses and folk-lore

S*kedgewith, blue poison, dog drake, common privet* are all names given to the plant in various parts. It is still possible to use wild privet as hedging in the garden. The flowers give off a pungent smell: it is quite strong in the wild – but one can imagine that if it was brought indoors the wild privet would create an unpleasant smell.

BISTORT AMPHIBIOUS

Persicaria amphibia: *Polygonaceae*

The plant: prefers having its roots in water – ponds, pond embankments and, sometimes, streams. Leaves float. Many stems arise from a single root – and they can be quite lengthy stretching up to three m.

The flowers: seen in mid-summer, they are small and pink on spikes of varying length. The flowers are five lobed, but this is difficult to confirm on the plant. A mid-summer flower.

The leaves: are narrow and usually hairless. The leaves float and to assist this in water of varying depth they are long-stalked.

Names, mythology, uses and folk-lore

Older plant lists will probably refer to the bistort as a Polygonum rather than Persicaria, which is its most recent name. The aquatic variety has been known as *amphibious knot-weed*. It is also called *long-rooted smart weed, water knotwort,* and *water smart weed.*

COMMON BISTORT

Persicaria bistorta: *Polygonaceae*

The plant: grows in the damp! Damp meadows, ditches and other similar places may be the host to this bistort. Can grow to about sixty cm in height – although in my experience in Northern England it is usually somewhat shorter.

The flowers: pink and seen through the summer until September – and sometimes longer. Like the aquatic variety the flowers are clustered together on spikes of varying length. Distinguishing the two bistort plants on the basis of the flowers alone can be difficult. Looking at the plant's habitat is usually the clue.

The leaves: approximate to an oval shape and only the lower ones are stalked.

Names, mythology, uses and folk-lore:

There are very many colloquial names given to the plant and often were given by cooks for the plant was used extensively in some households. These include *Easter ledges, gentle dock, poor man's cabbage, patience dock, red legs, pink pokers*. Other names include *great bistort, adderwort* and *snakeweed.*

In cookery, the plant has been a constituent of a bitter tasting pudding which incorporates the leaves, and also in dock pudding (or Easter ledge pudding).

Culpeper describes the types of ailment treated by bistort when the plant was taken internally. It resists pestilence and poisons, helps ruptures and bruises, stays fluxes and vomiting; in ladies it was used to treat menorrhagia (heavy periods). When used as a mouthwash it was said to be able to secure loose teeth.

Pechey described its value in episodes of vomiting which he attributed to the beneficial property of the plant it being an astringent. The plant's juices, when sprinkled in to a bleeding wound would also stop the bleeding, he said. For its internal use he gave the following recipe:

Leaves of bistort, tormentil, meadow sweet, Burnet, wood sorrel, burnt hartshorn (horn of deer) and shavings of hartshorn all boiled in three pints of fountain water and then three ounces of red roses would be added. The strained mixture would be given in a dose of six spoonfuls per day.

The use of deer horn is not often found in these old recipes – and I am not sure why it is there. Pechey specifies fountain water and not just any water. This may be a safety factor – spring water would have a greater chance of being clean and truly *potable.* Only red roses were to be used: again no reason for the red only rose – but perhaps this is because of the colour red which was perceived to be a force against evil (see the holly entry).

Pechey only refers to the greater bistort which is the common plant – but one suspects that any uses given to one plant would be matched by similar uses in the other.

BROAD-LEAVED DOCK

Rumex obtusifolius: *Polygonaceae*

The plant: grows in grassy fields and especially on their margins. It is a very common perennial plant which can be difficult to distinguish from other dockens such as water dock (q.v.). It is said to grow as high as one metre, but my experience is that it is usually a good bit shorter than this.

The flowers: arise from long spikes and can be quite densely clustered on the spikes. The flowering spikes are seen in the photograph. The seeds are arranged similarly. How many walkers in the country-side have taken a handful of the seeds and thrown them around? The flowers are seen in mid-summer from June to August.

The leaves: are long and broad – and in shape are more ovoid than anything else.

Names, mythology, uses and folk-lore

Butter dock (used as butter bur has been to wrap butter in some places for market), *kettle dock* and *bastard rhubarb* - this last name being used by Gerard.

The dock plant is very often conveniently found near stinging nettles – rubbing the leaf on a nettle sting reduces the discomfort from the sting – this has certainly been my experience. However, I am not the first to make this observation – Chaucer did it many centuries ago according to Grigson!

Allen and Hatfield have researched uses for the plant and they give details of its use in treating skin infections, including erysipelas, and for stings and burns. It has been applied as an infusion from the plant. It has been used similarly for the treatment of pain from shingles.

Culpeper describes the plant being used to treat scabs, itchy skin and "breaking-out of the skin" when used as an infusion after being boiled in vinegar. He claims that it could cure freckles. Culpeper was almost indignant that some people used the leaves to flavour meat stews: he said this resulted only in the stew becoming blackened. He went on to write of people using dock leaves in this way that reflected "pride and ignorance (a couple of monsters in the creation) preferring nicety before health".

Pechey is another herbalist who wrote that the dock plant was a useful herb – he recommended its use for choler (anger) and for "expelling the gravel" – presumably urine stones – and said that it was also good for "the itch".

Gerard recommended the plant for ring worm treatment and he recorded the treatment of a young boy with "ague" – fever – and who was cured by the dock leaf when it was put into a pint of ale and then given to the boy.

COTTONGRASS

Eriophorum species of the genus *Cyperaceae*

This book is designed to show wild flowers rather than grasses – but these two are quite striking when seen. They are commoner in the north of the country. Two types of cotton grass are shown here. One is the common cotton grass and the other probably the Hare's tail cotton grass. Both are perennials. I must reflect a little uncertainty in my own mind which is which for descriptions of the two plants do seem to vary a bit from one source to another. Possibly it does not matter for the uses to which cotton grasses have been applied to are few and usually described under the heading "cotton grass" only.

COMMON COTTONGRASS

Eriophorum augustifolium: *Cyperiaceae*

The plant: is a native to land areas which are marshy and generally acidic soils. The "cotton" appears in the early part of summer and generally before June. This grass was photographed on Holy Island in an especially boggy part of the Island.

The "flowers": the heads droop and the fruits of the flowers are much like balls of cotton.

The leaves: here the leaves seem short and dark green. Long thin leaves are often described, but not invariably. Clearly there are no long leaves here. **Should any reader know the plant, and that this one is not a cotton grass, it would be appreciated if you could tell me.**

HARE'S TAIL COTTONGRASS

Eriphorum vaginatum: *Cyperiaceae*

The plant: seen on heaths and moorland areas.

The flowers: grow at the end of a spike-like stem and the fruits of the flower appear afterwards – they appear somewhat brown with long cotton-like hairs.

The leaves: are very thin. **Again, if you feel that I am incorrect do please let me know and give me a reference to a good description of one!**

Names, mythology, uses and folk-lore

There seem to be no colloquial names for the plants which I have identified. Cotton grass has been used in Sussex to stuff pillows, and has also been used in wound dressings.

CAMPIONS

Caryophyllaceae

The campions are considered together for there are so many overlaps in function, custom and folk-lore. It can also be very difficult to distinguish one white-coloured campion from another.

RED CAMPION – Silene dioicia: (this plant is synonymous with melandrium rubrum).

The plant: found pretty much anywhere throughout the summer – but especially in hedges, grassland, light woodland, and roadsides. The plant is hairy and grows tall – in hedgerows up to one metre. Usually a perennial but sometimes behaves as a biennial.

The flowers: Male plants have smaller flowers than the female. Five deeply lobed red petals arise from a "swollen" calyx which is purple veined. The flowers are usually about two cm in diameter.

The leaves: hairy and arise from the stem in opposite pairs.

WHITE CAMPION – Silene latifolia:

The plant: Most often seen in grassy places and it can cross breed with the red campion producing pinkish flowers. Hairy! Again male plant flowers are smaller than the female. Grows to about one metre in height. It is either biennial or perennial.

The flowers: about twenty to thirty mm across and five petalled.

The calyx is "swollen" and purple veined. The petals are deeply divided. The flowers arise from a single stem branching from the ends of the main flower stems – there can be four or five flower clusters at the end of each stem.

The leaves: As with the red campion they arise in opposite pairs and are elongated oval in shape.

BLADDER CAMPION – Silene vulgaris:

The plant: Slightly smaller than either the white or red varieties growing to about seventy or eighty cm. Again is hairy and usually behaves as a perennial.

The flowers: deeply lobed five petals. Sometimes the flowers look to be in dis-array rather like the ragged robin. Usually about two cm in diameter. Shorter flowering season than the red or white lasting from June to August. The calyx is "swollen" – hence the term bladder – as with other campions and usually with purple veins.

The leaves: pretty much the same as the red and white campions arising in opposite pairs.

SEA CAMPION – Silene uniflora:

The plant: seen on cliff tops by the sea and in shingle by beaches. Much smaller than the other campions above, growing to about twenty five cm. A perennial plant which can grow almost in cushion fashion. Unlike the other campions is not hairy.

The flowers: white and about two cm in diameter. Five petalled with the petals sometimes overlapping each other. Flowers from June to August. The flower here was photographed on a low cliff in the Farne Islands - Inner Farne. The plant has a "swollen" purple veined calyx.

The leaves: similar to the other campions except seem thicker.

Names, mythology, uses and folk-lore

Both the red and white campions have sinister associations – the white campion, if picked, is associated with death and, more specifically, if the red campion is picked your mother will die.

Grigson is a rich source for colloquial names and associations – but so also are many internet sites. The web-site of plant folk-lore (http://www.plant-lore.com/1664/red-campion/) also gives a number of names by which the red campion has been known. These include *ragged robin, soldiers' fleas, soldiers' buttons, poor Janes, Red-riding Hood and Robin Hood, snake flowers* (would be attacked by snakes if brought in to the house), *mother* and/or *father die* and *mother-dee.*

Many of these names are also associated with the white campion and bladder campion.

The white campion is known by the following names – *Milk maids, pudding bags, mother-and-father die,* and another name on the plant lore website is *spattle poppy* possibly an onomatopoeic word associated with the noise made when the bladder is burst between the fingers although I believe that this was more commonly associated with bladder campion.

However there are innumerable names varying from *fat bellies* to *white-mint drops*, from *cock robin* to *(red) gramfer-greygles* and *granfer-griggles*. It can be a wonderful time spent researching the various names and it is well worth spending some hours on this.

Culpeper is, as ever, a rich source of information in describing the uses these plants might be used for, including a decoction of the plant being put in to either red or white wine and drunk – it will stop internal bleeding and would help to expel urine and also gravel and stones in the reins and kidneys. Such a mixture would purge the body of choleric humours, and would help those stung by scorpions and *"may be as effectual for the plague"*. It was also recommended by Culpeper for *old sores, ulcers, cankers, fistulae and the like and heal them by consuming the humours falling in to them, and correcting the putrefaction of humours offending them.*

The sea campion has very few references to it although the plant-lore website gives the following names: (if the flower is turned inside out it resembles) *a ballerina: deadman's bells* in Scotland and *devil's hatties*, also in Scotland are other names.

Other campions, which it is worthy looking out for, include the *moss campion* found mainly in Northern Scotland and several species of *catchfly* which tend to be quite localised to certain areas in the U.K. and the *night-flowering catchfly* which is quite common but only fully open at night, and therefore easily missed.

CHICKWEED

Stellaria media: *Caryophyllaceae*

The plant: A common plant of disturbed land and often seen in gardens. Stems are hairy on opposite sides. The plant can be prostrate although it is recorded as growing as high as twenty five or so cm. It is an annual.

The flowers: are small and rarely more than eight mm across and often smaller. There are five petals, deeply divided, and usually five stamens – but can be fewer or more. They are present all year round.

The leaves: Ovoid and are in opposite pairs. The lower ones are stalked.

Names, mythology, uses and folk-lore

For centuries the plant has been associated with chickens who pick at it for the seeds from it. Gerard records caged birds being given the plant in their cages and consuming it.

It is green all year round and the name *wintergreen* is sometimes applied to it. *Chickenweed* and *cluck weed* are found in many of the plant names.

Culpeper gives a variety of uses to the plant including applying the juice to the area of the liver will cure the heat of the liver. Also good for imposthumes, he said. Distilled water from the plant or the direct juice of the plant caused eye redness to resolve when dropped in to the eyes.

The juice boiled with hog's grease could help convulsions, cramps and palsy.

Using the drops as for the eyes but for the ears could resolve earache, and also when given appropriately could assuage the symptoms of piles.

Culpeper gave several complicated recipes, some involving oil from sheep trotters, being applied externally to the area causing symptoms could, after three applications, resolve any problem. At least that is how I interpret the text from Culpeper.

Allen and Hatfield record that the plant has been put to very many uses and attribute this to the ready availability of chickweed. In Northumberland it was described as being useful when boiled and eaten in cleansing the system and improving the complexion.

Given the large variety of uses attributed to the plant, for such diverse reasons, it may well not have been particularly indicated in any one disease process, although Allen and Hatfield describe its very widespread use in Ireland to reduce swellings.

COMMON MOUSE-EAR

Cerastium fontanum: *Caryophylaceae*

The plant: Hairy perennial plant of gardens and also of disturbed ground. Straggly and can reach about twenty five to thirty cm.

The flowers: are small and white about five mm across. There are five petals: they are very deeply notched. Seen throughout the summer from mid-spring until well into the autumn.

The leaves: narrow and in opposite pairs.

Names, mythology, uses and folk-lore

This is an edible plant like other chick-weeds. Better when boiled, according to the books – I have not tried it. Can also be used like spinach in soups and sauces.

However, this plant seems to have had no other uses attributed to it. References in the herbals to mouse ear are usually referring to the small hawk-weed like plant.

RAGGED ROBIN

Lychnis flos-cuculi: *Caryophyllaceae*

The plant: This is a plant which seems to create interest whenever it is shown to people. It can be so easily overlooked in damp meadows where it typically grows, although it does have obviously pink/red petals. It is a perennial, growing to about fifty to sixty cm in height. It is said to be common everywhere but changes in farming practices with land improvement by drainage have led to its decline - and in parts quite substantial decline - in meadows and pastureland.

The flowers: These are pink to red in appearance and difficult to gauge in diameter but upwards of four cm. A very careful look should show that there are five petals each divided into four deep and untidy-looking lobes.

The leaves: The leaves are narrow. They look for all the world like grass.

Names, mythology, uses and folk-lore

In many ways the name speaks for itself. The flower looks really untidy and ragged. The plant is, however, quite delicate. The flowers each have five petals which are each divided into approximately four untidy segments. On the stems the upper leaves are paired and this can be seen as they arise from the stem in the photograph. Gerard and Culpepper do not seem to mention Ragged Robin and this absence of the plant from herbals is confirmed by Allan and Hatfield, who refer to a solitary record only of the plant in folk medicine literature as being made into an ointment for snake bites. In Wales, Allan and Hatfield say it has been known as *Blodwyn Neidr* which, translated into English, means *snake flower*.

As ever Grigson gives it a wide variety of names. I recommend reference to Grigson if at all possible. Some of the names given by him include *Wild Williams, Shaggy Jacks, Ragged Willie, Meadow Spink, Cuckoo, Cuckoo Flower, Jonkeds,* and *Gypsy Flower* to name but a few. A look through this book will show that a number of plants have cuckoo names and robin names attaching to them – therefore there may have been some ancient folk-lore associations between all of these plants. As far as I am concerned it is a very attractive plant and well worth searching for. This specimen was found in a meadow in upper Weardale.

LESSER SEA SPURREY

Spergularia marina: *Caryophyllaceae*

The plant: An annual, prostrate spreading plant of sandy ground and dunes. The stems are usually numerous from any single root stock and can be as long as twenty five cm. the plant feels "sticky" and it is hairy. Also seen in some salt marshes and also alongside major roads that are salted in winter.

The flowers: small, five petalled plants where the sepals are longer than the petals. Usually no more than four or five mm in diameter. Flowers easily confused with the sand spurrey. Are seen through the entire summer from May to August. The flowers are pink but sometimes, towards the base of the petals, they become paler.

The leaves: are narrow and in opposite pairs.

Names, mythology, uses and folk-lore

Lesser sand spurrey, marsh sand spurrey and *salt marsh sand spurrey a*re other names given to the plant. This naming of the plant is quite confusing and it can be quite difficult differentiating the sea spurreys from the sand spurreys. An attractive plant, it is sometimes described as a "common weed".

Herbal uses in the past are few and far between, at least as far as I can find. Current herbals ignore the plant but there are internet references to Spergularia having been used to increase kidney excretions and thereby getting rid of gravel and treating nephritic colic.

Upper Weardale

SEA SANDWORT

Honckenya peploides: *Caryophyllaceae*

The plant: This is a low perennial plant and is generally seen on coastal shingle and near sandy beaches. This plant was seen on Holy Island. It is never more than two or three cm in height, although the stems may stretch out in horizontal fashion. It is seen throughout the United Kingdom but only in coastal districts.

The flowers: These are white, appear in the early summer and usually not more than seven mm or so in diameter. The sepals are longer than the petals, of which there are usually five.

The leaves: These are oval and quite fleshy in texture and appear quite starkly in opposite pairs on the stems.

Names, mythology, uses and folk-lore

The only herbal use that I can see this plant has been put to is described by Allan and Hatfield in their book. It was used against scurvy (anti-scorbutic) being gathered in the northern parts of Orkney.

SPRING SANDWORT

Miuartia verna: Caryophyllaceae

The plant: The plant is short in stature and grows quite specifically in two areas: one is in limestone rich soil and the other is spoil from lead mines. This plant was photographed in Slitt Wood where the Middlehope Burn runs down to Westgate in Upper Weardale and in an area where lead ore was sorted and stored in the 19th Century. This is a rare plant and occurs locally through the north of England, southern and mid Scotland and one or two other areas in the country, including upland Wales.

The flowers: The flowers are five petalled usually, although looking at the photograph - see over - it is clear that some of these flowers are four-petalled. They are small, being only five or six mm across in this example. Sepals are green and shorter than the white petals.

The leaves: As can be seen are narrow and are seen in whorl-like arrangements on the slender stems of the plant.

Names, mythology, uses and folk-lore

The Spring Sandwort seems to have no uses ascribed to it. This is perhaps unsurprising given its habitats which are very specific to the plant and usually only in upland areas. When seen it is a beautiful plant. It can be mistaken for mossy saxifrage but this particular plant tends to have the flowers arranged in upright fashion on the ends of relatively long stems. Spring Sandwort flowers tend to be found at the ends of long stems which are arranged along the ground.

Other sandworts to be looked out for and which you may well find as they are much commoner are the ***thyme-leaved sandwort*** and the ***three-nerved sandwort***. The flowers are very similar in appearance and size. The *thyme-leaved sandwort* can be found on dry, bare soils and the *three-nerved sandwort* in undisturbed woodland.

GREATER STITCHWORT

Stellaria holostea: *Caryophyllaceae*

The plant: A perennial spring flowering plant and also a very familiar plant on bank-sides beside paths, in hedgerows and lightly shaded woodland. Has rough stems. Can grow to about forty or fifty cm.

The flowers: these are five petalled and the petals are white. The petals are notched – sometimes quite markedly. The flowers are about two cm across but do vary in size.

The leaves: are narrow and grass-like and this makes the plant difficult to find when it is not in flower.

Names, mythology, uses and folk-lore

The name probably dates back some centuries to the mediaeval period when the plant was used to treat abdominal pains – or stitch pain. Gerard writes: "*They are wont to drink it in wine with the pouder* (sic) *of Acornes* (sic) *against the pains in the side and such like*. It is this which modern herbals describes as the plant's usefulness even to children, who are sometimes mentioned as chewing the flower to cure the stitch.

Some colloquial names include *snapjack, cuckoo's meat, lady's white petticoats, smocks* and so on. Grigson lists about one hundred names for the plant and he states that the plant also had magical properties. In some places children were afraid to pick it for doing so would make them more susceptible to snake (adder) bites. Some of the plant's names are suggestive of some possible shameful practices – *smocks, cuckoos, petticoats* and so on.

There are a number of species of stitchwort and you may well see them on country excursions or walks. The greater stitchwort is probably the commonest plant, but the others include:

- **Marsh stitchwort**: S palustris: seen as the name suggests in marshy areas, Like the greater stitchwort but a little smaller. Flowers in May – August. (not shown)

- **Lesser stitchwort**: S. graminea: grows in areas very similar to the greater stitchwort but the petals are usually more deeply divided, and the sepals are longer than the petals. It flowers from May – August.

lesser stitchwort

- **Wood stitchwort**:
  S. nemorum: s the name suggests this plant is confined to woody areas – especially damp woodland. Flowers May – August. (not shown)

- **Bog stitchwort**:
  S. alsine: grows in boggy areas and the flowers are never more than about six or seven mm in diameter. Like all the stitchworts it has five deeply lobed petals.

A dandelion meadow in Weardale
(see page 307)

BITTER-CRESS

Hairy ~, Wavy ~: *Brassicaeae*

It is convenient to consider these together.

Hairy bitter-cress: Cardamine hirsuta. This is a plant which grows well on disturbed and damp soil in dark areas, but is equally at home in pavement cracks and on any path. Usually quite small but can grow to about twenty five cm if undisturbed. It is an annual. The flowers are tiny – about three mm in diameter - and have four white petals. The leaves tend to be oval in shape, or even rounded, and are especially seen at the base of the plant with some stem leaves also.

Wavy bitter-cress: Cardamine flexuosa. Very closely related to the hairy bitter-cress and can be difficult to tell apart. The wavy usually has hairy stems whereas the hairy plant has no hairs in the stem! I have not been able to identify the reason for this apparent paradox. The flower of the wavy plant is four petalled and is the same colour and size as the hairy bitter-cress. The leaves are virtually identical.

One way to identify these plants from one another is to look at the number of stamens, which are the filaments plus the stigma. The wavy – usually has six with two being diminutive, but sometimes five. The hairy – usually has four – but also sometimes five. Here the plant has five, which does not help – but the stems are largely absent of hair and therefore this is the cardamine hirsuta but only just on the balance of probability. The wavy bitter-cress grows in dark damp places and does well in cracks on paths. The wavy is also usually quite small but can grow taller than the hairy – perhaps to about forty or forty five cm. The plant is regarded as an invasive plant in some places and control is attempted by pulling out the plant before it seeds. In Iceland it is an endangered species!

Names, mythology, uses and folk-lore

Very little is written about these plants – and what is seems to apply to both. Culpepper describes a black cress which I think may be the same as these plants – but I cannot be certain and there seems to be no reference to any black cress plant elsewhere that might have assisted. His descriptions states the seeds strengthen the brain and, when ground up in honey, the preparation is good for the cough, yellow jaundice and sciatica. He also describes that the herb, when boiled in to a poultice is excellent for inflammation of the female breast and the male testicle. Only one word springs to mind at this – ***ouch!***

Large bitter-cress – Cardamine amara. This is a further plant not shown here, but worthy of mention. It is another of the same family and is similar in some respects. Again it is a plant of damp and shady places – even marshy areas. However the flowers are much larger, up to about one cm, and have four white petals. It grows to about sixty cm. Like the others it is a member of the *Brassica* family.

ENGLISH AND DANISH SCURVY GRASS

Cochlearia anglicus, Cochlearia danica: *Brassicaceae*

ENGLISH: ***the plant:*** grows in seaside areas – tidal estuaries, cliffs, and walls. It is quite non-descript. Grows to about forty cm, although on this coastline in Northumberland the plants seemed shorter. Is a perennial plant usually although sometimes a biennial.

The flowers: are very small, up to about six or seven mm. in diameter and appear in clusters at the top of the plant**. *There are usually four white petals.*** Seen from May to October: this plant was photographed at Seaton Sluice just above the tiny harbour wall.

The leaves: the stem leaves seem to clasp the stem and their shape is best described as like arrowheads. Basal leaves are difficult to see because of the surrounding grass and other plants but these seem larger, being about two cm in length, and more kidney shaped than the stem leaves.

*Note: **Common scurvy grass** is very similar although usually a little taller in height. Flowers are roughly the same size – up to about one cm. in diameter but their flowering season usually ends in mid-summer. Leaves are narrow and on relatively long stalks. A late flowering scurvy grass is likely to be common scurvy grass.*

DANISH: *The plant:* seen near the coast in sandy soils, dunes and walls. However the plant has spread rapidly and lines many major roads and motorways which receive salt in the winter-time even in central parts of the country. Low lying and prostrate, this plant is an annual, and is photographed here next to the A68 trunk road near Riding Mill in Northumberland.

The flowers: are tiny and often not more than four mm in diameter. Flower from January to late summer and often appear as a white moss-like fringe to the road. They are white and have four petals.

The leaves: the basal leaves are said to be long-stalked but the plants shown here were prostrate and the leaves were mat-like on the plants and being roughly ivy-leaf shaped as shown here.

Names, mythology, uses and folk-lore

I have put all the plants under this heading – for the literature relating to scurvy grass seems usually not to identify a specific plant.. They are rich in Vitamin C – hence the use in treating/ preventing scurvy. Sailors setting out on voyages of indeterminate length might have taken with them dried scurvy grass to prevent scurvy – the disease of loose teeth, ulcerated and loosened gums, and extensive skin bruising. Gerard described the plant as being effective in curing sailors of this *"filthie, loathsome, heavie and dull disease"*. He went on to describe the signs in graphic detail: "*the gums are loosed, swollen and ulcerated: the mouth grievously stinking: the thighs and legs are verie often full of blewe spots like bruises: the face and bodie oft times pale and the fete swollen as in dropsie"*.

The taste of the plant is bad and was often masked with spices. An Oxford antiquarian, Anthony a'Wood suggested that it might be best drunk each morning. My advice is that you do not abandon your breakfast fruit juice – or breakfast fruit. It is thought that Roman legionaries used it under instruction from the Friesans for symptoms suggestive of scurvy. Scurvy grass sandwiches have been known!

Culpeper gave it a variety of other uses including opening up obstructions, and evacuating cold, clammy and phlegmatic humours from the liver. It also cleansed the liver, blood and spleen.

Other types of scurvy grass include the **Pyrenean** sometimes being seen in the North Pennines and in the Highlands.

CUCKOO FLOWER

Cardamine pratensis – *Brassicaceae*

The plant: prefers damp and grassy places – but it is really very common. It grows to about fifty cm in height and is a perennial plant. It is hairless.

The flowers: appear in April and flower through to mid-summer. The flower is about fifteen millimetres in diameter with four pale lilac or almost white petals.

The leaves: are mainly at the base of the plant and in meadow land may be very difficult indeed to see although there are also narrow stem leaves.

Names, mythology, uses and folk-lore

Another very common name for cardamine pratensis is lady's smock and this is the name with which I am more familiar. Cuckoo flower probably derives from the time the flower first presents – at about the time the cuckoo is first heard in spring. Smock may come from the word *smick* or *smicke*. Smick refers to amorous looks, and had rather coarse annotations – a bit of *skirt* or *smick*.

The web-based urban dictionary gives modern definitions of *smick* which do allude to slang of this sort.

It is unlucky to pick it. The plant was said to be sacred to fairies and bad luck would ensue if it was picked. Similarly, bringing it in to the house increases the risk of the house being struck by lightning. Pick it in Austria would render you to be bitten by an adder within the year!

I can find no herbal uses for it although I did come across one suggestion – and that is all it was – that it had been used to treat epilepsy at one time.

Shakespeare refers to lady's smock in Love's Labour Lost in the following poem about spring: *When daisies pied, and violets blue/, and lady smock's all silver white/, and cuckoo buds of yellow hue do paint the meadows with delight/, the cuckoo then, on every tree mocks married men, for thus sings he/: 'Cuckoo! Cuckoo, cuckoo!' O word of fear/, unpleasing to a married ear/. When shepherds pipe on oaten straws/, and merry larks are ploughmen's clocks/, when turtles tread, and rooks, and daws/, and maidens bleach their summer smocks/, the cuckoo then, on every tree/, mocks married men, for thus sings he/: 'Cuckoo! Cuckoo, cuckoo!' O word of fear/, unpleasing to a married ear.*

GARLIC MUSTARD

Alliaria petiolata: *Brassicaeae*

The plant: A tall plant very common in many parts of the country, although much less common in Northern Scotland. Grow to about one metre by the side of hedges and also on wayside verges, including roads. Looks quite spindly and delicate – but is an effective plant for self-survival. It is a biennial.

The flowers: have four white petals and the flowers are usually not much more than four mm in diameter. Appear from April to June.

The leaves: on short stems right up the plant's stem – are very roughly heart shaped with toothed margins.

Names, mythology, uses and folk-lore

The plant is also commonly known as *Jack-by-the-hedge* and *hedge garlic.* Other common names include *sauce alone, penny hedge, and poor man's mustard.* The descriptor garlic comes from the smell of the plant when the leaves or stems are crushed.

It has been used as a condiment, particularly with fish and mutton dishes, by cooking the food with the leaves to impart the "garlic", flavour. The young leaves have also been used in salads to garnish salads with a garlic odour.

Chewing the leaves helps cure sore gums and promotes wound healing.

Pechey gives a lengthy description of the herbal uses of the plant: when it is green it provokes urine and when dry expels poisons. Boil in wine or mixed with honey it can cure any cough. Applied it can manage putrid or malignant ulcers. If the leaves are boiled with water the liquid will manage colic, nephritic pains and the stone. The seeds rubbed and put up the nose provoke sneezing and purge the head, and the seed applied *to the bottom of the belly cures mother's fits.*

Culpeper tells the reader that the plant is controlled by Mars and therefore is good for chest diseases and hoarseness of the voice: using it for a short while can cure those who have utterly lost their voice, and almost their spirits also. The plant juice made up in to a syrup, or licking medicine, is also effectual for the same purpose and all other coughs, wheezing and shortness of breath.

The seed, said Culpeper, is good for sciatica, joint aches, ulcers and cankers in the mouth, throat or behind the ears – and no less for hardness of the testicles, or of women's breasts.

HEDGE MUSTARD

Sisymbrium officinale: *Brassicaceae*

The plant: A fairly tall straggling plant, growing to about one m. in height, and which must be synonymous with inconspicuousness. Yet it is a tough plant growing as it does on waste-ground and any disturbed soils. This specimen was on the perimeter of a car park utilising a few cm of tough soil between the car park and a perimeter fence.

The flowers: are small, being about two to three mm in diameter. They are in clusters at the ends of stalks: there are four petals and they are pale yellow in colour. Flowers from May to October.

The leaves: The leaves are basically lanceolate and narrow in appearance – but this is variable. They are usually quite deeply divided.

Names, mythology, uses and folk-lore

The plant is often home to caterpillars who feed on it. It is also possible for humans to feed on it for the leaves can be added to stews in the cooking.

It is said to have been good in chest diseases and for hoarseness of the voice. It can be made up in syrup as a licking medicine for these problems. Other uses for it include treating jaundice, pleurisy, back and loin pains, and for "torments" in the belly and colic. The seed is a special remedy against poison and venom, and is also said to be good for treating sciatica, mouth ulcers, swelling of the testicles and for diseases of women's' breasts.

Each plant can produce up to about one thousand seeds and when they are scattered after ripening can lie dormant in the ground for many years.

The honesty plant photographed here is growing alongside garlic mustard and cleavers on a roadside verge at the side of a wood.

HONESTY

Lunaria annua: *Brassicaceae*

The plant: commonly seen in hedgerows and by the edge of woods. Usually near built-up areas – the plant is considered a garden escapee, although it does seem to have successfully become naturalised. It is a biennial plant and it is quite hairy. The plant can grow to about one metre, or even more. Flowers in June through to the early autumn.

The flowers: are red/purple in colour and with four petals. Each is about two cm across and there can be clusters arising at the end of the stems. The fruits are circular or oval pods which are much used in dried flower decorations.

The leaves: are roughly ovate and toothed. They arise direct from the stems higher up the plant, but at the base of the plant they are stalked.

Names, mythology uses and folk-lore

Gerard gives the plant a number of names including *penny floure, money floure, silver plate* and *prickson-wort.* He states that the plant is good for wound healing and that it treated the "falling sickness" – probably epilepsy.

The near absence of folk-lore and the like may well be due to the fact that, in the wild, they are almost certainly garden escapees.

Upper Weardale early Spring

SHEPHERD'S PURSE

Capsella bursa-pastoris: *Brassicaceae*

The plant: A native of Asia-minor and the East of Europe it was probably introduced to Britain. It is now very widespread, being found from North Africa to the North of Europe and North America. It is a troublesome annual weed and difficult to eradicate because there may be several "harvests" of seed each year from each plant and these are scattered as the triangular-shaped purse like seed pods burst. Can grow to thirty or forty cm, but usually much smaller in Northern Britain. Can be found almost anywhere – in gardens, on paths, and on any disturbed land.

The flower: tiny – about two or three mm across with four white petals – usually two larger and two smaller. Flowers all year round.

The leaves: Some are lobed, some are toothed, some clasp the stem. All are green.

Names, mythology, uses and folk-lore

This plant is really pretty miserable to look at, and it seeks only to take over parts of my garden, but it has an amazing back-ground. Some of its names, widely quoted in many different places, include *naughty man's plaything* (a reference to the devil). Because of its purse-shaped seed pods there are a number of references to that including *pick pocket, pick purse, toy-wort*, and *purse flower.* The reference *to toy- wort* is possibly because it was the subject of some nursery games – a number of which were quite cruel.

Gerard refers to the plant and describes its property of "staying" bleeding in any part of the body regardless of the preparation and route of administration of the plant. Culpeper indicated that if the plant was bound to the wrists it would help the *yellow jaundice.* Culpeper seems largely to be in agreement with Gerard but adds that the juice instilled to the ears would ease the pains, noise and mattering therof. He also said it made a good ointment for treating head wounds. There are a number of references to the plant being infused as a tea to treat kidney problems. In the far East it is used as a food and often is served with rice in stir-fries. It has also been harvested as an animal food and is used in cosmetics.

The web-site http://www.botanical.com/botanical/mgmh/s/shephe47.html describes a large range of medicinal uses and it is worth consulting this site to obtain a fuller perspective of this most humble plant.

BIRD'S-EYE PRIMROSE

Primula farinose: *Primulaceae*

The plant: This lime-stone loving plant is rare and seen only in a few places in the North of England on open damp grasslands and heath. This plant was seen in a syke (small stream) in Upper Teesdale near Cow Green reservoir. Grows to about ten cm. Where seen it can be locally common. The plant will also grow in alpine-like areas of Northern Europe and Asia.

The flowers: each is about fifteen mm in diameter, and sometimes smaller. Deeply lobed five petals seen in groups – umbels - at the end of each stem. Usually flowers in June to July. The stems have a whitish coating.

The leaves: Oval shaped – some say spoon shaped – and basal. Usually whitish on the under surface.

Names, mythology, uses and folk-lore

There is a dearth of colloquial names presumable cause of its rarity in Britain, although the *Yorkshire primrose* is one such name as is the *Alpine primrose.*

It has few herbal uses specifically described – although it is probable that it has been used in the places where it grows in the same way as a primrose has been. Gerard is quoted by Grigson – "*it is a delightful flower which resembling the eie of a bird and hath moved the people of Northern parts (where it aboundeth) to call it Birds eine*". It was Gerard who described the plant and gave us its Latin name. This is a beautiful little plant and deserves to be seen – but please take care when you do find it.

The O.S. map reference is in the Landranger series Appleby, sheet 91, 815037

COWSLIP

Primula veris: *Primulaceae*

The plant: Commonly seen in areas where primroses grow – hedgerows, embankments (especially old railway embankments), undisturbed meadows – particularly on chalky/limestone soils. There has been a decline in recent years, possibly due to the cutting of grass verges or over harvesting of the plants for wine. Until the 16th century there was confusion over whether the primrose should bear the name of primula veris or whether the cowslip should do so. The cowslip won the day! They can grow to about twenty five cm although may be much smaller. Where present there can be very many.

The flowers: These are bell-shaped and hang down in bunches, or umbels, from the end of a stalk. There can be as many as thirty flowers on each stem, although usually many fewer flowers are seen. They are usually about ten mm across and appear in the spring time – about April.

The leaves: The leaves are basal on the plant and appear like a rosette. They are roughly oval in shape and can be quite long, wrinkly and covered in a fine down of hairs. They taper towards the tip.

Names, mythology, uses and folk-lore

There is a variety of historical and local names. The name we know it by presently may have come from its association with cow dung – or *cu sloppe/slyppe* in old English. Other names include *fairy cups* and *cow slap*. Grigson gives a splendid list of names from all over the country. Predominating in these are references to St Peter and to keys. One name for the cowslip is *paigle,* or key. Legend has it that St Peter, on being told that a duplicate key had been discovered for heaven, dropped his key in shock – and where it landed the cowslip grew. In German an old name is *Himmelschlüssel* (key of heaven). A fifteenth century use of the cowslip was to boil it in water and then drink the liquid in order to "cure" the "tremblynge hand" – this resulted in another name – palsywort. Almost certainly this was a treatment for Parkinson's disease. In common with the primrose a fine and delicate country wine can be made from cowslips. Shakespeare refers to the cowslip and its fairy associations in The Tempest when the following words are given to Ariel: *Where the bee sucks there suck I, In a cowslip bell I lie.........*

OXLIP – FALSE

Primula veris x vulgaris: *Primulaceae*

The plant: created by cross pollination of cowslips and primrose by insects – it is a hybrid of these two. It is found where the cowslip and primrose are seen together although it is much less common than the parent plants.

The flowers: These are primrose like, about fifteen mm across and, like the cowslip, there can be many such flowers in an umbel at the end of each flowering stem. The flowers are arranged circumferentially at the end of the stem unlike the true oxlip – a rare plant seen only in East Anglia – where the umbel is on one side only of the stem. Flowers in April/May just like the parents.

The leaves: These are exactly like the cowslip.

Names, mythology, uses and folk-lore

Bedlam cowslip, bullslop, covey keys, fairies' keys, milk maid, five fingers are all names described for the plant. I could find no herbal uses for the plant described although one suspects that there may be an overlap with the parent plants – including the wine making assuming enough of them can be found. Grigson is dismissive of the plant: he says it lacks the charm of either parent and of the true oxlip or Paigle.

Summer field and butterflies

PRIMROSE

Primula vulgaris: *Primulaceae*

The plant: a perennial plant of early spring. Grows to about twenty cm, although often smaller. Seen in hedgerows, damp grassy areas (if shaded) and also in woodland areas and banksides such as railway cuttings. Grows well in lime-stone areas and is not so happy on acidic soils. Has been declining – possibly due to climate change and some areas drying out, or due to over-picking, or other factors such as grass verge cutting, but the precise cause of the decline is just not certain. Is seen throughout the U.K. If a primrose is seen look around for cowslips and violets as well. This plant was photographed in Slitt Wood, near Westgate in Weardale, in May.

The flower: Single five-petalled flower to each stem. Pale yellow but with a more deeply coloured central area. About 2.5 cm diameter and seen in February to May depending on the part of the country where it grows.

The leaves: Oval and crinkly; about ten cm maximum length, but variable. Grow as a basal rosette.

Names, mythology, uses and folk-lore

Named from the Latin Prima Rosa – "First Rose" – but other names include *Easter rose, butter rose, May flooer* (in Northern Scotland and Shetland). Primrose and cowslip were, prior to the 17th Century, named interchangeably. This confusion of names may be the reason why primrose is called Schlüsselblume in German – the Key flower – for it is the cowslip which is associated with keys (Grigson). Many legends are associated with it: children eating the flower might see fairies; if a single plant grows near a hen house it is recommended to dance round it three time otherwise egg laying will be compromised. Leave a primrose on the doorstep will keep witches out.

Primrose has been used to make a delicate country wine. However large quantities are needed for this purpose and this should no longer be done with the wild plant. Culpepper describes it as being useful in a salve to heal wounds. Legend also has it that the primrose was used by Romans to treat malaria. Modern herbals seem to ignore the plant – just enjoy looking at it: when you see it spring will certainly have sprung!

SCARLET PIMPERNEL

Anagallis arvensis ssp arvensis: *Primulaceae (creeping)*

The plant: a hairless annual seen usually on disturbed ground although this plant was photographed in a sand dune area of Holy Island. Can form quite a spreading network.

The flowers: One cm in diameter, there are five petals which can be red, pinkish-orange and occasionally blue. Flower in mid-summer. The flowers open in sunlight only and the petals are fringed by hairs.

The leaves: are usually paired and are roughly ovoid in shape.

Names, mythology, uses and folk-lore

Many of the names are based *on time. The flowers open in sun-light by 8am, but close about 3pm each day.* Hence shepherd's watch/ clock, shepherd's calendar, wink and peep. Other names quoted in different places include *adder's eyes, grandfather's weatherglass*, and *weather teller*.

It is possibly best known from its adaptation by the fictional hero, the Scarlet Pimpernel, a story set in the French Revolution.

I could find no widespread herbal uses for the plant although references appear to the plant having been used against tooth-ache, depression (one colloquial name is "laughter bringer") and liver and kidney complaints.

Holy Island Castle and lobster pots

WOOD-SORREL

Oxalis acetosella: *Oxalidaceae*

The plant: This plant is a creeper essentially – but also a perennial. It grows in woodlands and hedges – especially where the land is damp and has been undisturbed for a very long time. I have seen it grow on the top of moss growing on old stones in Allandale and this plant was growing in the cleft of a dead Hawthorn bush in Slitt Wood, Upper Weardale. Here it is demonstrating its saprophytic character – it can live on dead or dying organic material. It is found throughout Great Britain and is best described as locally common. Where it seems to thrive especially well is in areas of stable land which is calcareous or neutral. Usually less than ten cm in height.

The flower: The flowers are rarely more than nine or ten mm in diameter and there are five white petals separate from one another and showing delicate lilac veins. Occasionally the plant has light pink flowers. The flowers are seen in April but can persist for a month or two. There is one flower per stalk. The flowers are hermaphrodite and can self-pollinate, but are also pollinated by bees and other insects.

The leaves: These are trifoliate, green and recumbent: they fold down at night. They can be hairy and the hairs are shown on the photograph. Each leaf is on a stalk coming from the base of the plant.

Names, mythology, uses and folk-lore

The plant has many colloquial names which include *wood-sour* and *ladies' clover. Hearts, cuckoo meat, cheese and bread, wild clover, crinche cranche* (Welsh – but I can find no similar words in Welsh dictionaries!), *sleeping beauty* and *sleeping clover*. In some parts it is known as the *Alleluia flower* for it appears at Easter when the word Alleluia re-appears in Church liturgy.

The leaves are eaten raw and are used as a food-stuff in their own right or as a way of "livening up" a green salad. The leaves have a high oxalic acid content which gives them a lemony taste – oxalic acid is a poison but a large quantity indeed would be needed to have any discernible effects. However, do take note of this. The flowers can be eaten raw as well – they make a good decoration for salads. It is also said to be especially good in fish sauces.

It has long had herbal properties: the plant has healing properties, including spiritual healing. Pliny recommended its use for "gastric conditions" but there are those who suggest that its oxalic acid content renders it no good for dyspeptic ailments. Pliny suggested that it could be used for even the most pestilential fevers. In the Hebrides it has been mixed in to a herb plaster for the treatment of scrofula (TB of the skin).

Not all botanists associate the plant with Christian liturgy and Christian spiritual healing. Lady Wilkinson describes its associations with Druidic practices and folk-lore – it is the Druids three-in-one mysterious secret. Where-ever Olwen, the Druid mother of Earth, trod, wood sorrel would grow in every footprint. Indeed some say that the plant has fairy associations and links with woodland elves.

Wood sorrel has also been displayed on British coins in association with Ceres, the ancient goddess of agriculture.

There is confusion over its association with St Patrick. Legends have it that Patrick, whoever he might have been, used the leaves as an aid in the teaching of the Christian Holy Trinity. It is claimed that this metaphor became the instrument of conversion for many Irish listeners to St Patrick's teachings. There has also been confusion over the association of the trefoil leaf with the Irish shamrock emblem. Whatever might be said of it the plant has a delightful flower, extremely delicate in nature, and a welcome reminder that spring is either on the way or has arrived.

Upper Teasdale

PROCUMBENT YELLOW SORREL

Oxalis corniculata: *Oxalidaceae*

The plant: this is a small plant, creeping and hairy. Usually seen in dry bare areas – this specimen was photographed on a hard, stony track. It is usually a garden escapee – but it is highly successful in escaping. Those I have seen are never more than about six or seven cm tall. The plant is an annual, forming each year from seed, but sometimes it forms a new plant from the stems of an existing plant.

The flowers: the bright yellow flowers are about six mm across. There are five petals and the flowers can be seen all summer.

The leaves: trifoliate and clover-like. The leaflets are notched imparting a heart shape to them.

Names, mythology, uses and folk-lore

The leaves are said to have a tangy flavour to them because of the oxalic acid found within them. Little is written about its herbal properties. The plant can become an invasive garden weed if not controlled (by pulling out) – and is spreading successfully in the wild.

FAIRY FLAX

Linum catharticum: *Linaceae*

The plant: A very delicate annual plant, growing no more than about ten cm tall. It grows on both dry and damp grasslands, especially where the soil is calcareous.

The flowers: are relatively small and usually about five mm in diameter. They appear at the ends of the stalks in loose clusters. The flowers can be seen from May to early autumn.

The leaves: grow in opposite pairs and are narrow.

Names, mythology, uses and folk-lore

This plant is easily overlooked unless it is in flower. It has been known as purging flax in some of the older herbalist's descriptions of the plant – but the plant has a link (seemingly very obscure) with fairies – hence the plant's present name. This name sounds a lot nicer than purging flax – but purging seems to have been its main herbal use: the bruised plant gently cooked in wine and then drunk, was a powerful purgative – but sadly it is also a powerful emetic (something causing vomiting). Allen and Hatfield quote a herbalist, John Quincy, who said that the flax was only of value in those with a strong constitution!

Regardless of these uses the plant is, quite simply, a beauty to look at.

Corbridge ducks by the Tyne

BUGLE

Ajuga reptans: *Lamiaceae*

The plant: An upright perennial plant which can reach twenty cm or so in height, although often smaller. Grows in grassy and woodland places – especially where the ground is damp and heavy. It puts out runners which themselves root to provide another plant. The stems are square in cross-sectional appearance and are hairy – the hairiness being on opposite sides rather than circumferential. The plants are often seen growing in large patches of them.

The flowers: violet in colour, sometimes closer to blue, they are about ten to fifteen mm long. The lower lip of the flower is paler. The flowers are quite typical of the labiatae family which includes the dead nettles.

The leaves: these are ovoid in nature and appear in opposite pairs: the lowest ones are stalked where they arise from the stems.

Names, mythology, uses and folk-lore

The name bugle is argued about in terms of its origin. It is suggested by some that it is derived from the Latin *ajuga* but others suggest that it is from the name *bugula* which is a name for a marine animal/plant that grows in shallow water, which was important in the available treatments used by apothecaries, and which can attach to ships fouling them. Conversely I have seen the term *bugula* being said to be derived from the plant *bugle*.

It has many colloquial names – unsurprising really given the widespread and common nature of the plant. Some of these are thunder and lightning, Gewitter Blume (thunder flower in German), babies' rattle or babies' shoes, and amongst other names it has been called dead men's bellows (Grigson).

The plant has had many herbal uses especially in healing wounds (a vulnerary application) when it might have been mixed with scabious and sanicle to treat not only wounds but also ulcers and bruises.

SELFHEAL

Prunella vulgaris: *Lamiaceae*

The plant: a low lying plant that puts out creepers which root. Seems to prefer calcareous soil and is fairly common in grassy places and by paths in woodlands. Grows to about fifteen cm in height and can easily be confused with bugle. It is hairy and also is a perennial plant.

The flowers: are about twelve mm long give or take a mm or two. They are blue in appearance and can be quite densely packed in a cylindrical fashion at the ends of stems. Flowers are seen in the spring time. The bracts are purple in colour.

The leaves: these are ovoid and arise in opposite pairs.

Names, mythology, uses and folk-lore

Prince's feather, proud carpenter, pickpocket, heart of the earth are all names said by Grigson to have been used in the North of England for this plant.

Gerard knew the plant as Prunell or Brunel and said that it "growth very commonly in all our fields throughout England".

Gerard gave some uses to the plant. For example he wrote: "The decoction of the plant made with wine and water, doth joine together and make whole and sound all wounds both inward and outward, even as Bugle doth. He went on to say that when it was mixed with oil of roses and vinegar and then applied to the forehead would cure headaches. He said that the plant was as good as bugle in what it did and "there are not two better wound herbs, as hath bin often proved".

Culpeper described largely similar uses for selfheal and concluded by giving a proverb of the Germans, French and others, is verified in this: "That he needs neither physician nor surgeon that hath Selfheal and Sanicle to help himself." Perhaps our political overlords are not aware of this – and just as well I hear you say!

WILD THYME

Thymus polytrichus: *Lamiaceae*

The plant: The plant is a delightful splash of colour often in quite bare places such as heath land, or coastal cliffs and in the upper regions of the Pennines. There is a considerable quantity of wild thyme growing on the sand dunes at Holy Island.

The flowers: These are about three to four mm in length and are a vivid pinkish purple. The flowers are seen in mid summer between June and August.

The leaves: are on short stalks and are opposite one another growing from the stems. The stems themselves are hairy and in common with many of the labiate plants the stems are four-sided with the angle between each side roughly conforming to a right angle.

Names, mythology, uses and folk-lore

An internet search relating to wild thyme reveals more entries on the first page retrieved naming restaurants rather than plants. Perhaps this is a whimsical look to the herbal uses of thyme and particularly their use in cooking. Be that as it may, the wild thyme is a bonus on any country walk. It brightens the path side, never growing more than a few centimetres in height. Books tell one that it is faintly aromatic of a typical thyme smell but I must confess that I have never been able to smell it when on a country walk, although thyme in my garden has a strong, and pleasant, odour. I have heard wild thyme referred to as mountain thyme by some people but I think that this is an error. It can certainly be found on upland areas but is equally at home at the coast.

The Wildlife Trust website relating to wild thyme describes it thus: "*walk across a chalk grassland in summer and its fragrance will punctuate the warm air around you – a delightful sensory experience.*" Another website relating to wild thyme is Herb2000. com and this gives some of its other names, which include *creeping thyme, mother of thyme,* and *wild thyme.* However the Latin name is also given and here it is recorded as thymus cerpyllum. It is this name which is used by Grigson in his description of wild thyme. However the description given by Herb2000.com seems to be challenged by Richard Maybee in Flora Britannica in which thymus cerpyllum is a thyme confined to sandy heaths in West Suffolk and Norfolk. The wild thyme is said to be thymus polytrichus and this plant, shown here, can be seen in much of the country.

A number of uses for wild thyme have been described by various authors and, in summary, these include antiseptic properties, anti-spasmodic properties, properties of diuretic function and its use as a headache cure and as a sedative. As a result it has been used in treating sore throats, 'flu and colds, whooping cough, bronchitis, chest infections and for managing intestinal colic and pains that arise from cramps and muscle spasms. It has been used either in ointment form or as a medicine to take by mouth. Maybee states that in the Western Isles the wild thyme was put under the pillow or drunk as an infusion to prevent nightmares or otherwise to give a restful sleep. Thyme tea was popular throughout the Highlands as an everyday beverage. Its name in Shetland is *tae-girse* which Grigson states is the equivalent of tea grass. Wild thyme is also one of the herbs of St John in French tradition. Wild thyme is described as being a constituent of posies used by Judges: it is also in the Maundy Thursday posy which the sovereign of the day would carry when handing out the Maundy money. This was to prevent the carrier of the posy from contracting infectious diseases from the poor.

However, being more practical in this modern era, wild thyme is still a valuable herb food and can be used in cooking in place of the garden varieties of thyme when they are not available. Given the usual availability of "domestic or garden" thyme picking the wild variety is not a good idea.

WOUNDWORT

Lamiaceae

HEDGE WOUNDWORT - Stachys sylvatica (above)

The plant: grows on disturbed soil, in hedges, on roadsides, in woods – usually where the ground is damp. Can reach up to sixty or seventy cm and is a perennial. The plant is covered in hairs. It is a perennial.

The flowers: about fifteen mm long and purple, or reddish purple, in colour. There are white markings on the lower lip. They appear in long terminal spikes in a series of whorls round the stem and without proper leaves from June until about October.

The leaves: are roughly oval and toothed. They are also stalked.

MARSH WOUNDWORT – Stachys palustris (below)

The plant: A common plant of damp places: the one photographed here was in a bunch of the plants growing in a ditch on Holy Island. Is a very sturdy plant and can grow quite tall – up to one m. is not unusual. Is a perennial. Unlike the hedge woundwort it is odourless.

The flowers: are about fifteen mm long and appear in long terminal spikes in a series of whorls. Each whorl has a pair of leaves beneath it. Flowers in the summer from June to September. The flowers are about twelve mm long and usually are on the pink side of purple. They have white markings.

The leaves: are lanceolate and long: they are unstalked usually.

Names, mythology, uses and folk-lore

The herbalists tend not to consider the plants separately.

The plants have a reputation for stopping bleeding when packed in to wounds. Gerard called the plant "Clowne's" woundwort. Gerard met a man when on a trip to Kent who had cut his leg when using a scythe. The wound was down to bone and the labourer had simply packed the wound with woundwort and it was now healing very well. Gerard offered to treat this man on a pro bono basis – the man refused saying he was doing the treatment well enough. Gerard thought the man a "clowne" for refusing such help – and named the plant "clowne's" woundwort.

Gerard went on to treat a man with a deep chest injury with the plant: he used the following recipe – four handfuls of the herb, stamped, and put in a pan: added to this was four ounces* of Barrow grease, half a pint of olive oil, and then the mix was boiled and strained. To the strained fluid he put in two ounces of turpentine. Put portions of this to the wound and also put portions in to a ***good*** claret and boiled it with a handful of woundwort leaves and four ounces of honey. Two spoonfuls of the liquid were given each morning – in wine and tempered with a little sugar. The chest wound healed, he said.

* a table of old weights and measures is included in the glossary.

Culpeper confirmed the value of woundwort in healing wounds and stopping bleeding – but he also added that when taken orally and also applied to the area it would cure ruptures.

Other names include *deaf nettle, swine's beads, roughweed, cock head* and *hound's tongue* (Grigson).

Another plant to look out for is the similar **betony** which has flowers of a deep reddish purple hue, and possibly the **field woundwort**, but which is commoner further south than the North of England. Other similar plants are either very rare or seen only in Southern England – these include **black horehound, wild clary, meadow clary,** and **limestone woundwort** (very rare).

Marsh Woundwort

WHITE, RED AND YELLOW DEAD NETTLES

Lamium album, L. purpureum, l. galeobdolon and/or argentatum: *Lamiaceae*

The plants: these are common in much of the country in many situations including grassland, edges of woods, roadside verges, and any disturbed ground. The white variety grows to about forty cm and the red to thirty cm approximately, although most of those seen by me are rather smaller. They are perennials.

The flowers: the white is about thirty mm long and the red about half that length. The white has a hairy upper lip, or hood, the lower lip is toothed. The red is much the same but with purplish flowers and normally no hairs. The flowers of each plant are arranged in whorls about the stem. The plants are in flower from March through to mid or even late autumn.

The leaves: are in opposite pairs on the stems and the white dead nettle has leaves which are green and are roughly ovoid in shape and are toothed. The red variety has leaves which are a mixture of green and red-purple more towards the stalk end of the leaf. Again they are ovoid, more or less, and are toothed.

Names, mythology, uses and folk-lore

Gerard used to call the dead nettles "Archangel". The origin of the name seems to be lost in obscurity – but it probably arose from Archangelus which is also a word derived from the Greek. Gerard it was who called the nettles Archangel rather than Archangelus. Just as an Archbishop is a very high ranking Bishop, the Archangel is a high ranking angel. Grigson wondered if the name arose because these were kindly nettles – they did not sting. A not unreasonable thought, I suspect.

Gerard said that the flowers could be baked with sugar to make a sugar rosette.

Herbal use can be made of the distilled water from boiling the plant in the water. Drunk it will make the heart merry and gives a good facial colour and refreshes the "vitall" spirits.

Culpeper adds that the archangel stops hardness of the spleen and, in ointment with hog's grease, will cure the King's Evil, and will also ease pains from gout and sciatica and could also treat green wounds and old ulcers. He says it has its chief use in women for it is under the influence of Venus.

Pechey also describes its value in treating the King's Evil but he uses some mystique in this for he first bled the sufferer then purged him/her before giving a nutmeg full of a very complex recipe which includes the archangel plant among many others including Venice treacle, yellow pill of oranges, Diascordium (itself a herbal mixture), candied ginger and nutmeg, roof of Spanish Angelica, powder of cats' eyes, bark of the pomegranate, red coral, bole-armenick, gum Arabic and syrup!

The white dead nettle is sometimes called *Adam and Eve*: turn the plant upside down and you will see in the flower a black and a yellow stamen lying side-by-side – hence *Adam and Eve*.

Also consider the yellow Archangel: the plant photographed is almost certainly a garden escapee which has become successfully naturalised. The “wild” variety usually has green leaves, but the variety shown here, with the variegated leaves will usually have arisen from a garden somewhere and spread. The Latin name is **Lameastrum galeobdolon** for the truly wild variety and **Lamiastrum argentatum** for the garden escapee. The folk-lore surrounding the yellow variety is mingled with the folk-lore of the group.

COMMON/STINGING NETTLE

Urtica dioica: *Urticaceae*

The plant: A tall plant that seems to have a liking for the sides of country walks and pathways. Characterised by an unpleasant sting which comes from the hairs on the plant where-ever they are sited – on stems and leaves.

The flowers: appear catkin like. The flowers are male or female according to the plant from which they are derived and appear throughout the summer. The seed appears, macroscopically at least, to be like the flowers.

The leaves: are in opposite pairs, are hairy and are about seven or eight cm long. They are pointed and are borne on short stalks.

Names, mythology, uses and folk-lore

Where man goes the nettle is sure to follow! It appears in his rubbish, in his garden, even on the house walls – and is difficult to eradicate. It even appeared in the Americas where the Pilgrim Fathers first landed and within a short time of doing so.

In Scandinavia legends have it that the nettle marks the place where elves live, and that the nettle can also protect milk from being affected by trolls or witches. The plant stings most when lightly brushed, but much less if grasped tightly – hence the expression – **"grasp the nettle".**

However in some country areas of the U.K. nettles have been used with milk to produce some fine and delicate cheese. One such is Northumbrian Nettle cheese. It is well worth buying if you see it.

Nettle fibres have been used extensively in cloth making – some were cultivated and harvested for this purpose.

Some herbals refer to its value in treating rheumatism, urinary problems and sciatica. It acts as a diuretic and is also capable of being produced in to drinks which will contain high levels of iron. Has been used in a poultice to treat eczema. The nettle can even be eaten in salads although I have never tried this. However nettle beer exists and many will have tasted this drink.

Sir John Harington (also spelled Harrington) (4 August 1561 – 20 November 1612), of Kelston, was a courtier, author and master of art, popularly known as the inventor of the **flush toilet**[Wikipedia]. He became a prominent member of Queen Elizabeth I's court, and was known as her "saucy Godson". But because of his poetry and other writings, he fell in and out of favour with the Queen. He translated, in 1608, the Medical Poem of Salerno of which the following is a subtitle: "Physical observations for the perfect Preserving of the body of Man in continual health." This is taken from verse 117:

Though Nettles stink, yet make they recompense,
If your belly by the Colic pain endures,
Against the Colic Nettle-seed and honey
Is Physic: better none is had for money.
It breedeth sleep, stays vomits, phlegms doth soften,
It helps him of the Gout that eats it often.

Nettle stings can be ameliorated by rubbing dock leaves on to them. This very long-standing custom and practice has been questioned and some say it is of no benefit. I must say that a conveniently placed dock plant, green-leaved, always eases the irritation of the sting if applied soon after the sting.

If you spot a smaller nettle – say no more than about forty or fifty cm tall - then you may have found the *small nettle (Urtica urens).* This is difficult to distinguish from the common nettle other than by height. This is widespread and locally common.

BINDWEED

Convolvulus and Calystelgia species: *Convolvulaceae*

HEDGE BINDWEED

The plant: as the name suggests this is most often seen growing in hedges and can become upwards of three metre in length. It climbs in anti-clockwise fashion and is a very vigorous plant. It grows rapidly, is invasive, and if it is found in the garden – or is planted there – it is almost impossible to eradicate. Found almost everywhere in Britain other than the North of Scotland.

The flowers: are up to six or seven cm. in length and are trumpet shaped. They are white in colour and appear from June to September.

The leaves: are pointed and roughly arrow-shaped.

LARGE BINDWEED

Not shown here but appears even more vigorous than the hedge bindweed growing to four m. in height and having larger flowers. Otherwise there is little difference between the two other than that the large bindweed is seen mainly in the southern part of the country.

FIELD BINDWEED

The plant: grows along other plants in fields reaching up to three m. in length. Flowers either basically pink or white. Like other bindweeds the flower is funnel or trumpet shaped. The pink flower also has white stripes very similar to the sea bindweed. Is invasive and very vigorous, and is difficult, if not impossible, to eradicate. Flowers in June to September. The plant is usually a creeping one, but can climb when near a hedge.

SEA BINDWEED

The plant: grows on sand-dunes and also on shingle. The one photographed here was in shingle at the top of a beach on Holy Island. The flowers appear from June to August and the flowers are smaller than the other bindweeds usually from about three to five centimetres across. Like other bindweeds they are funnel or trumpet shaped. The pink flowers have usually five white streaks on them. The leaves are usually kidney shaped rather than the more arrow shaped of the others. The plants can be lengthy. Uncommon except on coastal places. The position of this plant photographed made it more likely to be a sea bindweed, but the markings of the flower make it more like a pink field bindweed.

Names, mythology, uses and folk-lore of all these plants

The field bindweed is from the convolvulus family whereas the hedge, sea and large bindweeds are from the closely related calystelgia family. All the plants wind around others for support and this property gives some of the colloquial names commonly associated with them. Such names include *devil's guts, bedwind,* and *robin-run-in-the-field* and their vigorous nature along with the difficulty associated in their eradication also gives rise to such names as *hell weed* and *devil's thread.* Despite these names the flowers are quite majestic in appearance. The plants also have a powerful purgative effect (Allen and Hatfield) as well as having been described as being cures for warts. However it is never recommended to grow them in the garden, despite them looking attractive in garden centres – once planted you will have them for life. (See also the entry for honeysuckle).

HONEYSUCKLE

Lonicera periclymenum: *Caprifoliaceae*

The plant: A common and much loved climbing plant of hedgerows and woodland. It is woody and perennial. The scent from the flowers is especially recognisable on a warm summer evening and may be evident before the plant is seen. It grows clockwise up the hedges, bushes and trees. Flowers in June to August. This plant was photographed in a country lane in North Yorkshire. Well over fifty different species of honeysuckle are known and some are shrubby rather than being climbers. Many are evergreen.

The flowers: are arranged in circular fashion at the end of the flowering stem. They are trumpet shaped and usually pale yellow at the end of a similarly coloured stem or one that is more nearly purple as shown here. They can be anything up to four or five cm in length. The seed fruits are a vivid red.

The leaves: are roughly oval in shape.

Names, mythology, uses and folk-lore

Very few herbal uses seem to have been attributed to the honeysuckle, although Allen and Hatfield describe its use in Ireland for inflammation of the mouth and for the *privy parts of men and women* probably suggests it was used for what would today be recognised as thrush. Burns, whooping cough, TB and erysipelas have also been treated with honeysuckle in Ireland – although it has been used for adder bites in Devon and treating sunburn in Scotland. The berries should regarded as if poisonous.

Names often include *suck, suckle* or *scent* and, rather confusingly, there are references to it being called *ladies' finger*.

Flanders and Swann, two great comedians and songsters, wrote about the honeysuckle and the bindweed (q.v.) in a song called Misalliance. The words are produced here:

The fragrant Honeysuckle spirals clockwise to the sun
And many other creepers do the same.
But some climb anti-clockwise; the Bindweed does, for one,
Or Convolvulus, to give her proper name.

Rooted on either side a door one of each species grew
And raced towards the window-ledge above;
Each corkscrewed to the lintel in the only way it knew,
Where they stopped, touched tendrils, smiled, and fell in love.

Said the right-handed Honeysuckle
To the left-handed Bindweed:
'Oh, let us get married
If our parents don't mind; we'd
Be loving and inseparable,
Inextricably entwined;
we'd live happily ever after,'
Said the Honeysuckle to the Bindweed.

To the Honeysuckle's parents it came as a shock.
'The Bindweeds', they cried, 'are inferior stock,
They're uncultivated, of breeding bereft;
We twine to the right-and they twine to the left!'

To the clockwise Honeysuckle:
'We'd better start saving,
Many a mickle maks a muckle,
Then run away for a honeymoon
And hope that our luck'll
Take a turn for the better,'
Said the Bindweed to the Honeysuckle.

A Bee who was passing remarked to them then:
Tve said it before, and I'll say it again;
Consider your off-shoots, if off-shoots there be,
They'll never receive any blessing from me!

'Poor little sucker, how will it learn
When it is climbing, which way to turn?
Right-left-what a disgrace!
Or it may go straight up and fall flat on its face!'
Said the right-hand thread Honeysuckle
To the left-hand thread Bindweed:
'It seems that against us
All fate has combined ...
Oh my darling, oh my darling
Oh my darling Columbine,
Thou art lost and gone for ever,
We shall never intertwine.'

Together they found them the very next day.
They had pulled up their roots and just shrivelled away,
Deprived of that freedom for which we must fight-
To veer to the left or to veer to the right!

DOG'S MERCURY

Mercurialis perennis: *Euphorbiaceae*

The plant: A lover of woodlands but also grows under hedges. Does best on undisturbed ground where it spreads out readily. Can form extensive beds and when that happens it is incredibly difficult to eradicate by any means. One of the main enemies of gardeners it is one of the most vigorous of weeds. The plant spreads by extension of the roots. If brought indoors a foetid smell becomes recognisable. If the rhizomes are included the plant can be upwards of a metre long.

The flowers: these are tiny and rarely more than about two mm in size. They are yellow and appear on spikes in the separate sex plants. The flowering season is relatively short from March – April.

The leaves: these are oval in shape.

Names, mythology, uses and folk-lore

The term "dog" implies here that it is a lesser herb. Taken by mouth it induces vomiting, and it can be used as a laxative in enema form. One of its colloquial names is *Bad Henry* – possibly after a German name for the plant – *Böser Heinrich*. Other names include *adder meat* and *snake's meat*.

Some names, according to Grigson, include the name *Boggart*. *Boggart* is a name for household spirit or a malevolent goblin which inhabits fields and marsh-lands. Other names in this group include *bug, bugbear, bogey man* and the like. The *Boggart* causes milk to become sour, things to just disappear, dogs to become lame and, in the fields, the *Boggart* abducts children.

The plant is poisonous in all its parts although the dried plant is said to lose some of that toxicity.

BELL HEATHER

Erica cinerea – *Ericaceae*

The plant: A heather that thrives on open moorland and often this means very harsh environments especially in winter. Bell heather is more suited to dry places. Grows to about fifty cm in a shrub-like fashion. Very dramatic when seen in flower on moorland.

The flowers: roughly bell-shaped and about five mm long. Reddish-purple.

The leaves: small, green and almost wiry to the feel.

Names, mythology, uses and folk-lore

Socially used to be a very important plant – used in bedding, both for cattle and humans, used also as a fuel. Heather thatching to rooves has been used and there have been heather thatches in Northumberland. Are fashioned into brooms, and bee keepers favour the darker honey produced from heather (usually ling). Heather has also been used in the production of ale and www.rampantscotland.org traces the history of this back to 2000BC. Heather is also a good feed-stuff for sheep.

Allen and Hatfield describe its use as a mild soporific and also as an agent to treat consumption. In some parts it has been used to treat stomach upsets and diarrhoaea.

Grigson lists the various names that have been used for *bell heather*, including one that I have used since a child – *purple heather*. However his comments about heather are dominated by his statement that it has been used, when in blossom, by bad artists and makers of post-cards!

Arguably the best source I have found on bell heather is www.arkive.org/bell-heather/erica-cinerea.

Despite Grigson's comment, heather clad uplands, whether bell heather, or simply heather, are most dramatic when in flower.

HEATHER (LING)

Calluna vulgaris: *Ericaceae*

The plant: Evergreen shrub of high moorlands, especially when they are acidic. Also grows in woodland. Grows to about fifty cm.

The flowers: are small and usually about four to five mm in diameter. The flowering time is relatively short from August to September. This plant was photographed on Muggleswick Fell in the Pennines where there are hundreds, if not thousands, of acres of the plant giving a wonderful purple colour to the otherwise bleak landscape – as well as providing cover for grouse and other birds (as well as adders).

The leaves: Short and narrow from the stem. Almost furry in nature.

Names, mythology, uses and folk-lore

There is really nothing to add to the description given for bell heather. There are records of properties in the moorland areas of Northern England having thatched rooves of heather. It is good bed material where no other soft mattressing is available. It also gives food to sheep and the honey made from heather by the bees is especially good to eat, and much prized by many.

Other names include *bazzom, he-heather, dog heather* and *mountain mist*.

By the Pennine Way, Teesdale

HEATH MILKWORT

Polygala vulgaris: *Polygalaceae*

The plant: said to grow to twenty cm. I must confess that I have not seen one more than about twelve – to thirteen cm. A perennial, it trails on the ground and as can be seen from the photo it is hairless. Almost indistinguishable from the common milkwort – but it is smaller and the lowest leaves at the base of the plant are opposite pairs in the heath milkwort.

The flowers: the blue flowers appear in May/June and can be seen until the autumn. They are in spikes of up to ten in number. The common milkwort may also be pink or even white. They are about six mm long.

The leaves: are narrow and the ends are pointed – this compares with the chalk milkwort in which the leaves arise in alternate fashion on the stem.

Names, uses, mythology and folk-lore

The plant was prized by cattle owners for it was thought it increased milk yields in their cattle which ate it. Allen and Hatfield describe its use to promote the flow of human breast-milk after child birth. Allen and Hatfield are cautious in attributing uses to the plant saying that many of those described may be arising because of confusion in identifying the plant – often the plant was probably spurge (a Euphorbia). Culpeper ignores it and Gerard simply says that it usually flowered in Rogation* week. One of its names is *Rogation flower* but this is probably true only for the southern parts of the U.K. Further north its late flowering may mean that it is too late for Rogation in some years. However the plant is woven in to garlands to be used in Rogation week processions.

Gerard also said that it was sometimes sold by the "herbe women" of Cheapeside calling it hedge hyssop (this is a plant of the Gratiola group, sometimes known as the herb of Grace, and scarce in the U.K. if it grows here at all). Confidence trickery is not a modern problem!

* Rogation is a Christian celebration. Rogation comes from the Latin "rogare" which means to ask. God's blessing is asked for the seed and the soil, and for those who labour in the fields - and for all of God's creation. It is often associated, where practical, with a marking of the boundaries of the Parish – "Riding the Bounds" is a tradition in many rural areas. The date varies in the Christian calendar – for example, in 2014, the Rogation days were May 26th, 27th and 28th and they always occur just before Ascension Day which in 2014 was on May 29th.

BITING STONECROP

Sedum acre: *Crassulaceae*

The plant: Perennial plant that can only be described as mat forming where-ever it grows and flowers. Grows on stony ground, sand dunes, walls and stone rooves. Present throughout much of the U.K. and is common in those areas it is seen.

The flowers: are about one cm in diameter. There are five bright yellow petals and the flowers seem densely packed together.

The leaves: are small and close to the stem. They appear quite fleshy and are clustered closely together.

Names, mythology, uses and folk-lore

Culpeper describes only one stonecrop in detail in terms of its herbal uses and calls it sedum reflexum. A look on the internet shows a whole library of sedum-like plants, all different, all with the name sedum reflexum – one looking very much like biting stonecrop. So there must be some uncertainty over the naming attributions of stonecrop. Biting stonecrop is sedum acre.

Culpeper gives the plant a legion of uses. These include using it "to stay defluctions from the eyes". Other uses given by Culpeper include stopping haemorrhage, both internal and external, and it can be used in the treatment of cankers, fretting sores and ulcers. Culpeper recommends its use for choler (*anger* or *ill-humour)* and for tertian agues. What Culpeper means by this I do not know but probably it relates to the intermittent fevers associated with malaria. It may also be a link to one other name of the plant – Prick madam which comes from the French name Trique madam.

He also states that the bruised plant applied to the place affected will treat King's evil, knots and kernels of the flesh, including piles.

Allen and Hatfield say that juice from the plant has been used to treat dermatitis and shingles, and also for getting rid of intestinal worms. Uses against kidney stones have also been described.

Sedum album is a close relation to biting stonecrop – this white stonecrop was used as an aphrodisiac in France.

There are a number of other closely related plants – all sedums. The stonecrop family is widely scattered throughout the U.K. and often relatively uncommon. Many plants have become naturalised, possibly from gardens. These other plants include: *white stonecrop, rock stonecrop, English stonecrop,* and *orpine (sedum telephium).*

WHITE STONECROP

Sedum album: *Crassulaceae*

The plant: a plant with similar places of growth to the biting stonecrop – rocky ground, old walls – and has similar properties in that it is a mat-forming perennial. Never more than about ten or twelve cm tall. This plant was photographed on Holy Island. It is evergreen and perennial.

The flowers: Five petals in a star shape, and are white but may also show some pink. They are about eight mm in diameter.

Flowers seen over summer from June to October.

The leaves: fleshy and green intermingled with a red-brown colour.

Names, mythology, uses and folk-lore

The white stonecrop seems not to be mentioned separately from the yellow – and when that happens usually any uses the plant may have been given are likely to be much the same between the two types of stonecrop.

Other stonecrops you may find are the *hairy* and *rock stonecrops*, all with five petals, and the *yellow stonecrop* again with five petals. They all favour rocky places or walls on which to grow, with the hairy species preferring damp rocks or walls. The plants tend to be relatively uncommon apart from the *biting stonecrop*. Happy hunting!

Lower Middlehope Burn in Slitt Wood, Westgate

BLUEBELL

Hyacinthoides-non-scripta;

HYBRID BLUEBELL

Hyacinthoides non-scripta x H. Hispanica: *Liliaceae family*

The plant: the familiar bluebell is seen in woodlands mainly where it can form whole drifts of flowers in spring time. Often seen in areas which favour Ransoms. Two varieties are described in the country-side – the true British bluebell and the Spanish bluebell. Cross breeding occurs between the two and the resulting hybrid may be more like one or other of the parent plants.

The flowers: The Hyacinthoides-non-scripta British plant has pendulous flowers which are quite narrow, (above left) are bell shaped and up to about twenty five mm in length. The flowers are usually blue, but white or pinkish flowers are seen. The petals are six in number and are recurved at their ends. The Spanish variety (H. Hispanica) is also bell shaped but here the flower is broader, comparatively speaking, and the petals are not recurved. Again these flowers are blue usually. The hybrid plant has flowers which are roughly between the two main varieties – but the contribution from each parent does seem to be variable. The plant shown here is probably a hybrid from the two main varieties – the H. non-scripta x H. Hispanica. The anthers here are blue but may be pale yellow/whitish in appearance. Flowering time is April to May.

The leaves: H. non scripta leaves are long and narrow, and all are basally arranged. They are rather glossy and never more than about fifteen mm wide. The Spanish variety also has lengthy leaves, all basal – but these are much broader. One photograph shows a near certain British flower (top left picture page 115) and the other leans more to a hybrid variety rather than a true Spanish type – but the differences can be very difficult to tell.

Names, mythology, uses and folk-lore

A plant as ubiquitous as the bluebell can be expected to have many names – and it does. *Crow's feet, blue goggles, Gowk's (cuckoo) hose* (in Scotland) and, in Welsh, *croeso haf* – welcome summer. Again Grigson is an encyclopaedic reference for plant names. The plant is seen in Western Europe so does not appear in the early Roman or Greek writings. Its name stems from the fact that it appears hyacinth like. In chapter 15 of his herbal, Gerard writes of the hare-bell – but almost certainly he is referring to the bluebell.

He says that the root is full of a slimy juice which can be used to set feathers in arrows instead of glue, and the same slime can be used to set books. Gerard calls it Hyacinthus Anglicus – but he does make reference to Dioscorides suggesting that the plant was more widely known. The roots, when beaten and applied with white wine, hinder hair growth!

It is written about by many authors, including Shakespeare, and Gerard Manley Hopkins. Hopkins wrote: ***"In the little wood opposite the light they stood in blackish spreads or sheddings like spots on a snake. The heads are then like thongs and solemn in grain and grape-colour. But in the clough through the light they come in falls of sky-colour washing the brows and slacks of the ground with vein-blue, thickening at the double, vertical themselves and the young grass and brake-fern combed vertical, but the brake struck the upright of all this with winged transomes. It was a lovely sight. The bluebells in your hand baffle you with their inscape, made to every sense. If you draw your fingers through them they are lodged and struggle with a shock of wet heads; the long stalks rub and click and flatten to a fan on one another like your fingers themselves would when you passed the palms hard across one another, making a brittle rub and jostle like the noise of a hurdle strained by leaning against; then there is the faint honey smell........" (Hopkins, 1871).***

(http://www.leavesnbloom.com/2012/05/bluebell-woods-dalcrue-perthshire-what.html)

Folk-lore sometimes links the plant with orchids (q.v.) symbolizing sexual powers.

BOG ASPHODEL

Narthecium ossifragum: *Liliaceae*

The plant: is relatively small – perhaps no more than fifteen to twenty cm. in height. In the early summer it is green, but in the autumn, at the end of the flowering season, it turns orange-brown as here. Found as the name suggests in bogs – but particularly in upland areas. The plant grows in Upper Teesdale but is uncommon in the Pennines. This particular one was photographed on a wind-swept moor-land bog above Applecross in N.W. Scotland where the plant is commoner. Grows outwards by underground creeping rhizomes and also by seed spread.

The flowers: mid-summer flowering, the flowers appearing on spikes. Star shaped when open: they are about twelve mm in diameter. The anthers are quite prominent – orange coloured.

The leaves: The leaves are basal and very narrow.

Names, mythology, uses and folk-lore

Essentially this is a plant of Northern Uplands from Wales and Northern England northwards. Colloquial names emanate mainly from Scotland – such names included *yellow grass, moor golds,* and *moor grass.*

Said to cause brittle bone disease in sheep – but this is probably incorrect. The Latin name, ossifragum, means "weak bone". The probable origin of this story is that sheep eating a calcium-poor diet are likely to develop bone weakness, and *N. ossifragum* favours acidic, low-calcium soils.(Wikipedia)

I have found no evidence of any herbal uses for the plant.

RAMSONS GARLIC

Allium ursinum: *Liliaceae*

The plant: Ramsons garlic is a plant of damp woodlands. Grows best on calcareous soils and can form "carpets" of flowers in woodlands around the trees and lining woodland paths. It is a plant of spring time – and is often in flower at the same time as bluebells. It has been a plant well known for centuries.

The flowers: The flowers are seen in rosette-like structures at the ends of the stem. The stem is three-sided and quite delicate. They are usually about fifteen mm in diameter. Seen in April to May, and the seed fruits are capsular.

The leaves: Long, somewhat ovate leaves which are all basal.

Names, mythology, uses and folk-lore

A variety of local names are recognised. Many have a reference to the plant's pungent smell – Ramsons in flower in a damp wood emits a characteristic and pungent smell of garlic – such names include *stinking Jenny, stink plant, stinking lilies, onion flowers* and *onion stinkers.* I have always known the plant as *wild garlic. Allium ursinum* is a name given to the plant because the bulbs have been favoured by brown bears in Europe – and also by wild boar. (Ursinum means, literally, of a bear – hence the name in some parts of *bears' garlic*).

It is always worth a trip to a wood where the wild garlic grows in spring-time when the flowers are evident. The dramatic change to the woodland floor can be remarkably striking. A very good spot in Tynedale is Allan Banks – but there are many other sites.

Although not the same as the well-known French garlic, the plant is used in cooking. Recipes usually suggest picking the leaves before the plant flowers provided there is an abundance of the plants in the area. The leaves go well with sea-food, can liven up a dull salad, and, finely chopped, are useful in fish sauces. The flowers can also be eaten. In general it is said that the wild garlic is milder than the cultivated varieties of garlic.

Herbal uses are few and far between. Neither Culpeper nor Gerard describe any such uses. Dieter Podlech, in his book on Herbs and Healing Plants, describes it as being useful in the treatment of digestive problems, high blood pressure, rheumatism and asthma.

There are various suggestions put forward to try and explain why the plant is so pungent in smell – for this is its characteristic and which should allow easy differentiation from similar plants such as Lily of the Valley – perhaps this pungency gives the plant some protection from being eaten by grazing animals (other than bears!).

Allium sativum – the well-known food garlic – has a wide history of use dating back to Hippocrates (fourth century b.c.). This plant is not considered further here.

WHITE WATER-LILY

Nymphaea alba: *Nymphaceae*

The plant: Perennial plant that grows new leaves each year. The leaves float and are water oxygenators. The plants will only survive in water – and in water up to about three m. deep and always in either still water in ponds or in very slow moving water in streams or rivers.

The flowers: large and very showy appearing in June and usually some are still there in August. The flowers may be tinged with pink. They are about twenty five cm across and have a variable number of petals – usually about twenty five. The flowers are on stalks that take them to the water surface or just above it.

The leaves: these are large and float and can be anything up to thirty cm across. They are roughly circular in outline.

Another commonly seen lily is the ***yellow variety***. This is ***Nuphar lutea.*** The plants are similar except that the flower petals are fewer in number and the flowers are smaller at about six or seven cm across. The flowers also stand well clear of the water surface on their stalks.

Names, mythology, uses and folk-lore

Culpeper gives both the white and the yellow lilies similar functions. He recommends that a syrup containing the flowers helps to procure rest and settle the brain of frantic persons, by cooling the hot "distemperature" of the head.

The root boiled in wine and water, and the decoction, drunk, is good for the hot urine (presumably a urinary infection). A distilled water of the flowers and other material is commended to take away freckles, spots, sunburn and morphew from the face and other parts of the body.

Grigson refers to the rhizomes (roots) being steeped in tar and applied to the head for curing baldness.

WILD DAFFODIL

Narcissus pseudonarcissus: *Liliaceae*

The plant: Like the garden daffodils the wild daffodil grows from a bulb. It is quite small in stature growing to about forty or fifty cm. at most. It is a plant that has a most unusual distribution with large groups of daffodils being seen in a few well known but scattered areas. Thus they are seen in the Lake District, Gloucestershire, Wales and at Farndale in the North York moors. Left alone the plant tends to increase in number locally. Seen in open woodlands, damp areas, grassland and, as in the Lake District, in rocky soil. It is the county plant of Gloucestershire and the national flower of Wales.

The flower: easily recognisable but the wild daffodil does have particular features to look out for – most notably the outer segments which are pale yellow and the trumpets which are a very deep yellow. They appear in March to April according to where they grow – they come later in the North than the South. The flowers are about five cm across and at least as long down the trumpet. There is one flower per stem. The photographs here are taken by the River Dove, or its tributaries, in Farndale.

The leaves: these are long, lanceolate and narrow: they all emerge basally, as does the flower stem. They are essentially green in colour – with a greyish tinge. The leaves die down after flowering finishes.

Names, mythology, uses and folk-lore

The wild daffodil is often known as the *Lent Lily* given that it usually appears in flower in Lent. Grigson gives a comprehensive list of other names - these include *asphodel* from the Mediaeval Latin affodilus, *Easter Lily, fairy bells, Easter Rose, hoop petticoats, sun-bonnets* and many others. A name used in Wales meaning welcome to spring is *croes aw gwanwyn*. Daffy down lily has been in general use as a name – and this name certainly was used in old English poetry *Daffy down dill is come to town, with a yellow petticoat and a green gown*. The plant is poisonous in all its parts – this has limited its usefulness! The poison is an alkaloid known as **lycorine**. However, there are reports of it being used as an emetic and a purgative – but most certainly not to be used in that way! Lady Wilkinson indicated that the French had allowed alcohols distilled in Algeria from the daffodil be admitted to France without payment of any excise duty.

The wild daffodil has been written in to many poems – perhaps most notably by Wordsworth in "*I wandered lonely*" or "*Daffodils*". The daffodils in Wordsworth's poem are almost certainly the wild daffodils around Ullswater. Shakespeare, Coleridge, and Gerard Manley Hopkins are among a number of others who have all used the daffodil in their poetry.

Returning to the name, it probably comes originally from the Greek *asphodelus* through the Latin *asphodilus* and then to the Mediaeval Latin as *affodilus* and thence *daffodil*. Lady Wilkinson in her long account of the daffodil is sure that the name derives from the old-English name *affodyle* which she says signifies *that which cometh early*. Daffodil eventually emerged from this name. Lady Wilkinson also links the daffodil in "modern mythology" i.e. the nineteenth century, as being sacred to St Perpetua (a third century Christian martyr) – but no reference is given for this.

One aspect of the wild daffodil which intrigues me, and for which my researches have not yet found a satisfactory explanation, is why it is seen in such profusion in the isolated sites where it appears in England and Wales (it is rare in Scotland). One explanation might be that it is an escapee from plantings in mediaeval times – for example the monks at Rievaulx Abbey are alleged by some to have planted the wild daffodil that acclimatised in Farndale. If so then they planted the same species exactly that grows wild elsewhere in Britain and Europe – so this is an improbable suggestion. Best just to enjoy it for its beauty – just as good as any modern hybrid!

YELLOW IRIS (YELLOW FLAG)

Iris pseudicarus: *Liliaceae*

The plant: A relatively common perennial waterside plant – or even aquatic plant. Will also grow in very damp soils. It is a most striking plant growing to about one m. in height and by a combination of seed spread via water and spread from the rhizomes a single plant may come to be responsible for an area of plants twenty m. across. In some places it can be quite invasive almost blocking up streams. In this event, the plant can be difficult to remove for the rhizomes are likely to be quite thick. This plant was photographed on a Wildlife Trust Reserve in Northumberland, growing in a pond in the centre of a field. It is a perennial plant.

The flowers: large, up to ten cm across, and are at the ends of the stems. The flower is a striking yellow colour with purplish lines. In the top picture yellow iris is growing amongst mimulus.

The leaves: are thick, green and shaped a little like a spear or sword.

Names, mythology, uses and folk-lore

Names include: *Yellow flag, sword grass* (Northumberland), *seggen (after sedges), Skegg* in Yorkshire, *Flags, Segg* (Anglo-Saxon for a short sword),

In France it is a herb of St John's Eve. In Ireland bunches of it are hung outside at the feast of Corpus Christi – they are said to ward off evil. The rhizomes produce a black ink and dye. The roasted seeds are said to resemble coffee. The juice is an astringent and can stop bleeding.

Gerard calls it water flags (or floure de-luce). The roots, clean washed, and to which has been added rose water and then laid on a facial bruise takes away the blue-black colour in two days. It is necessary to put a silk cloth between the bruised area and the herb to avoid inflaming the skin.

Culpeper emphasises its astringent effects. Distilled water from the whole herb can heal watering eyes. Helps spots about the eyes. Same water can treat breast inflammations. "Helps foul ulcers in the privies of man and woman – although an ointment from the flowers is more effective"!

Has been used as an enema on Skye and in Northern Scotland used for sore throats, inflammations and toothache. A teaspoonful of the juice poured to both nostrils produces a copious flow of mucus and saliva. In Orkney the juice used to be "snorted" up the nose. (Allen and Hatfield).

In the South of England it has been used for kidney problems and in the 19th C. an ointment from the flowers was used as a cosmetic.

In Ireland it was used to treat mumps as well as toothache – and in an area just S.W. of Ulster has been used for jaundice! (Allen and Hatfield)

However the plants do contain some harmful glycosides – herbivores usually will avoid eating it.

LORDS AND LADIES

Arum maculata – *Araceae*

The plant: Grows to about thirty – fifty cm and most commonly seen in wood-land, but also in the hedgebacks. It is one of the earlier flowers of spring, appearing in April to May. It tends to occur in clusters but is a perennial. The root can penetrate the soil deeply and is a rich source of starch.

***The flower*:** appears soon after the leaves grow. They are quite complex. There is a long "hood", sometimes called a spathe, which is pale green (almost a yellow-green) and edged in purple: from the base of the hood protrudes what is called a spadix (the hood may be called a spathe) – this can be up to about 15 cm in length in my experience. The flowers themselves are at the base of the spadix and well-hidden – there is a ring of female flowers and above them male flowers: above these is a ring of hairs. The hairs appear to trap insects – especially midges – and they acquire pollen from the flowers, that from the male flowers pollinating the female flowers before the insects escape through the hairs. In the autumn the stems are covered in red berries which are the fruits of the plant.

The leaves: appear before the flowers and are oval in shape, more-or-less, and green usually spotted with purple marks. There are two or three to each plant and normally whither before the berries mature.

Names, mythology, uses and folk-lore

I have always called this plant arum lily – although it is not recognised as a lily. The name lords and ladies is said to resemble male and female genitalia, and probably alludes to copulation. The plant has many names attaching, some very ancient, and the following are a selection which appear often and in many places - *Adam and Eve, snake's head, jack in the pulpit, cows and bulls, starch root, cuckow (sic) pint* and *snakes head* among many others. *Starch wort* is another name and is a reference to the high starch content of the roots.

The plant is seen throughout Northern Europe and is quite distinctive. Despite this it seems to have had few herbal uses, possibly because of its reputation of being a skin irritant. Gerard said (of its roots which are full of starch) it is *hurtful to the hands of laundresses – for it choppeth, blistereth, and maketh the hands rugged and rough and smarting*. Culpeper gives no internal uses for it but recommends it for removing skin blemishes such as freckles, and for curing the pain of gout, all when applied to the skin.

However, the berries are poisonous and, if swallowed, can cause throat swelling, severe heart burn and vomiting. I remember my days as a casualty officer in hospital when children appeared quite regularly after swallowing the berries.

Lady Wilkinson refers to a German superstition which states that if a part of the plant is put in to the shoe of a young man going to a dance, and he says: *I place you in my shoe; let all young girls be drawn to you* that he would then secure to himself any partner he wished. Her account of the cuckoo pint is arguably the most telling in her book. She also calls the plant, the *priest's pint* which does seem a somewhat incautious reference*, although it is also a name listed by Grigson among around one hundred others. She refers to the *reverent feeling of our own peasants towards the plant* and then describes some of the superstitions the plant carries and some uses, including its use (the powdered plant) as a cosmetic in Paris at the time.

This plant is fascinating and is well worth researching by any reader of this book.

**pint* is an abbreviation for *pintle* an old English word for penis.

HOLLY AND IVY

HOLLY

Ilex acquifolium: Acquifoliaceae

The plant: Holly grows in woodland and hedgerows and has become a plant strongly associated with Christmas. Usually it is seen as a shrub but can grow up to about ten metres. ***The flowers*** – white - are seen in June and are four-petalled being arranged in clusters. Each flower is only a few mm diameter. The seed is a bright red berry and is a characteristic feature of the plant. ***The leaves*** are also a characteristic feature – glossy, thick, evergreen, often prickly and slightly darker on their upper side. Very common!

IVY

Hedera helix: Araliaceae

The plant: Seen, like the holly, in woodlands, hedgerows and scrub areas. Self-clings by a sucker-like root to buildings, trees and the woodland floor. ***The flowers*** are small, seen in globular-like heads, and appear in the late autumn. They form dark, almost black berries. ***The leaves:*** like the holly they are glossy, tough and evergreen – but are not prickly or spiked. They are actually lobed but this is not always an obvious feature. The leaf veins are yellowish.

Folk-lore, mythology, uses and names of both plants

Names: As ever Grigson is a good reference source. However, there are relatively few colloquial names. The holly is most commonly known in old legend as *holly,* or *prickly holly.* I grew up calling it *berry holly.* Ivy is almost universally known as ivy – *ivery* and *bentwood* seem to be the commonest other names both now and in the past.

These two plants seem inseparable in some myths and folk-lore and so are described together – and relatively briefly. Culpeper is, as ever, full of uses for both plants – especially the **ivy**. He reminds the reader of its many associations with alcohol. For example Dioscorides, he said, recommends red wine steeped leaves of ivy for the treatment of diarrhoea ("lask") and the "bloody flux". Berries taken in wine will break kidney stones. Leaves boiled in rose water, and applied to the temple, will ease headaches. Culpepper also quotes Pliny who said that the berries can treat jaundice and, if taken before a hard-drinking session, protect from drunken-ness and will treat those who spit blood. Leaves boiled in wine will cleanse "old filthy ulcers", and will heal wounds, ease scalds and treat burns. Culpeper states that there is "much apathy between wine and ivy – if one has a surfeit by drinking of wine" the speediest cure for the consequence is to drink a draught of the same wine "wherein a handful of ivy leaves, being first bruised, have been boiled".

Holly berries, says Culpeper, expel wind and are good for colic. Taken ripe and undried, on a fasting stomach, they are good for getting rid of phlegm. The dried berry powder is recommended for bloody fluxes and terms in women. The dried berries bind the body! Pliny, Culpeper said, suggested that the branches of the holly wrapped as a garland around a horses neck will protect it from lightning and witchcraft.

Allen and Hatfield describe the use of holly in treating chilblains in some parts of the country. If the chilblains are beaten with a sprig of holly until they bleed, the circulation is improved. (I wonder if this just identifies those in whom the circulation of the skin is quite good, and this is shown by the bleeding, so the chilblains are more likely to heal – just a thought!). Powdered holly berries applied to the skin in an ointment with lard is also described by Allen and Hatfield.

Drinking from cups made from ivy help treat whooping cough. Ivy leaves used topically for eczema, corns and warts is also recorded by Allen and Hatfield. I recommend very strongly perusal of this book by Allen and Hatfield (see bibliography). You will then discover that the leaves and berries have also been used in the treatment of mumps, and also as an abortifacient (in Wiltshire).

Margaret Baker's fascinating book on plant folk-lore describes the appearance of holly where Christ's footsteps had been. She describes also the importance of holly in determining who would rule the household in the year following Christmas. A smooth-leaved holly wreath favoured the woman as ruler and prickly holly favoured the man. Greatest harmony would be found when equal quantities of each variety of the plant were brought inside. She has advice on when to bring the plant indoors – it should not be brought in before Christmas eve and must not be removed before 12th night. Baker is yet another writer who says that holly protects against storms and sorcery, and she confirms the widely held view that a holly collar would protect horses from witchcraft. Baker also confirms Culpeper's descriptions for ivy in its uses for drunkenness and she describes ivy in its prevention of scurvy.

Further research reveals the evergreen ivy as being a symbol of everlasting life. The ancient Greeks dedicated it to Bacchus and the leaves were generally associated as being a symbol of friendship. Sadly, ivy is not always associated with friendship. In the second book of Maccabees, found in the Old Testament Apocrypha, there is an account of the revolt of the Maccabean Jews in Judea against King Antiochus. Chapter 6, verse 7, describes what Antiochus demanded of the Jews: *On the monthly celebration of the king's birthday, the Jews were taken, under bitter constraint, to partake of the sacrifices; and when a festival of Dionysus was celebrated, they were compelled to wear wreaths of ivy and to walk in the procession in honour of Dionysus.*

Grigson describes how holly was worked into Christian folk-lore. Holly had the perceived property of keeping demons out of the church building, and the plant itself brings together the crown of thorns and blood. The flowers of holly are white and as white as the lily flower: this representation of purity became linked with the Virgin Mary and Christ's birth: the bright red berries are reflective of blood, and the prickles sharp as any thorn, and the bark tasting as bitter as any gall, are all emblematic of Christ's Passion. The Advent wreath often contains holly - the circle of the wreath symbolizes the eternal cycle of the seasons while the evergreens and lighted candles signify the persistence of life in the midst of winter. The Advent wreath comes from a Lutheran tradition.

The holly and the ivy were plants of considerable importance in folk-lore and applications. Grigson describes them as being plants with power. Holly and ivy were used to protect against witchcraft and they were said to be effective in keeping goblins out of the house. The red berries of holly were "powerful" forces against evil – the colour red protects against evil. Which of the two is the more powerful, or important, has been considered by poets and song-writers especially in mediaeval times, with different conclusions being reached.

Ivy flowers

Holly has long been associated with the winter solstice by Druids, and to the Romans it was a plant associated with Saturn. The ivy is associated with everlasting life and with wine and Bacchus. Together they were fashioned in to wreaths in the dead months of the year.

Where, or how, does our famous carol, The Holly and the Ivy, fit in? The carol is almost exclusively about the holly and how it is the preferred, and supreme, tree in the wood – *the holly bears the crown*. Probably written in the 16th Century this carol may follow an earlier carol describing the *"contest of the holly and the ivy"* in which the holly represents the male, and the softer ivy the female: the song may reflect the rivalry between man and woman. (See www.landscaping.about.com/od/holidayplants1/a/hollyand_ivy_2.htm). Holly and ivy have been part of the Christian church traditions and remain so today – "T*he holly and the ivy"* carol remains one of the favourite songs we sing in churches at Christmas.

ROSEBAY WILLOWHERB

Chamerion augustifolium: *Onograceae*

The plant: is instantly recognisable when in flower with the very tall flowering spikes appearing on the road side verges and hedge backs. It is also one of the first plants to appear when ground has been cleared of buildings and it now lies bare and fallow (ie: waste ground). It seems to grow on pretty well any soil and for me it is the harbinger of autumn – the cottony seeds being blown about on the wind. Some wonderful spiders' webs can also be seen on the willowherb on a mellow, damp autumn morning. Grows almost to a standard adult height. It is very common – and very beautiful.

The flower: pinkish-purple and with four petals which are variably notched. Grow on tall flower spikes and often more than sixty or so to each stem, although flowering occurs in the lowest flowers first.

The leaves: The leaves are lanceolate and are arranged in spiral fashion on the stems.

Names, mythology, uses, and folk-lore

This plant is a success story in the plant world. It seems capable of growing anywhere and on a breezy day in September the air is thick with the cottony seeds being blown about. The flower spikes are a real treasure for the eyes to see.

Gerard described it as a goodly garden plant. Grigson suggests that the plant was mainly a local plant that did not spread until the Industrial Revolution occurred and railways were constructed, factories were put up and taken down, and woodlands were felled to provide trees needed in construction. The plant spread widely in the mid nineteenth century.

Where the name comes from is rather obscure. It is thought that the term *rosebay* is related to the Oleander plant – also called Rose Bay – but that seems improbable at least on appearance alone. In Sweden it is called *Himmelgraes – Herb of Heaven*. Sometimes called *fireweed* in the United States. Other names, among very many which are listed by Grigson are *tame withy, flowering withy, ranting widow* (*widdy* comes from *widdy* or *willow).*

Linnaeus (1707-1778), Swedish botanist, zoologist and physician says that the leaves can be eaten as a vegetable and the young shoots may be served up like asparagus.

No doubt other uses have been applied to the flower – if so I have not come across them – apart from, of course, its use as a decorative plant.

GREAT (HAIRY) WILLOWHERB

Epilobium hirsutum: *Onograceae*

The plant: Around two metres tall this is a magnificent plant of hedgerows, river banks and any damp area. It is a perennial and, whilst it is widespread, it is not in my opinion, as common as the rosebay willowherb. This plant was photographed in a road-side grassy ditch in North Yorkshire.

The flowers: Appear in mid-summer and are in clusters at the end of the plant. The flowers are about two to three cm. in diameter and are a deep purple-pink colour. There are four petals each having a small notch in its outer edge. The centre of the flower is paler and the stigma is four lobed. The seed pods contain cotton-like seeds which blow in the early autumn breezes.

The leaves: these are narrow and ovoid, and are hairy.

Names, mythology, uses and folk-lore

Gerard describes several types of willowherb. The description which relates to what I believe is the great willowherb is worth repeating: *This being thought to be a bastard kinde, is a.....most goodly and stately plant. The branches come out of the ground in great numbers, growing to six feet, garnished with brave flowers of great beauty consisting of four leaves* (petals) *apiece, having some threds in the middle of a yellow colour. The cod* (seed pod) *is long and full of downy matter which flyeth away when the cod is open."*

Gerard also gives the information that the smoke from burning the *herbe driveth away serpents and killeth flies and gnats in the house.* (Quotations here use Gerard's own spellings).

Culpeper does not seem to describe the plant.

The plant is sometimes known by the name *codlins and cream.* Other names widely mentioned include *currant dumpling, gooseberry pie, love apple* and *sod apple.*

BROAD-LEAVED WILLOWHERB

Epilobium montanum: *Onograceae*

The plant: this is a plant of woodlands and hedges rows. It grows a little taller than the pale willowherb. A perennial it is almost devoid of hairs.

The flowers: about six mm in diameter and pale pink in colour. Flowers in the earlier part of mid-summer.

The leaves: are more of an ovoid shape and broader than the pale willowherb leaves.

Uses: the only use I could find for this plant is presented in Allen and Hatfield's book – and that is it has been used in Austrian herbal medicine. There seem to be no other uses described.

PALE WILLOWHERB

Epilobium roseum: *Onograceae*

The plant: A non-descript plant growing to about seventy cm or so and which is seen in damp ground. This plant was photographed amongst trees in my garden in July. I am not totally certain of the name for the petals are pinker than might be expected but the leaves are correct for pale willow herb. Probably commoner in the south of England.

The flowers: very small and only about four to six mm in diameter. Usually are nearly white when first appear (these here were tinged with pink) and turn a pale pink as they get older.

The leaves: are narrow.

This plant seems to be largely unloved by herbalists.

Note: there are many varieties of willowherb and some varieties are virtually indistinguishable from others. Unusually, when willow herbs are presented on internet sites, the authors of these sites sometimes come to a flower's name on the basis of one or two features of the plant "ticking the boxes" rather than being able to find a full set of typical findings. I think that is true of these willow herbs.

PURPLE-LOOSESTRIFE

Lythrum salicaria: *Lythraceae*

The plant: grows to about one metre or, sometimes, a little higher. Found in damp areas – this was one was photographed, in Stratford on Avon, in a damp area below a wall on the banks of the River Avon – but they can be seen pretty well anywhere except the far north of Scotland in the right environment. It is characterised by tall and lengthy flower spikes. The plant is hairy and is a perennial. Numerous stems seem to grow from a single root.

The flowers: are purple, about one cm across or a little more and have six reddish-purple petals.

The leaves: are up to seven or eight cm in length and are more nearly lanceolate than any other shape. They grow from the stem in opposite pairs.

Names, mythology, uses and folk-lore

Some of the names that have been given to the plant are shared by many others – for example *long purples* is also a name given by Shakespeare to early purple orchids (q.v.). Other names include *ragged robin, soldiers* and *willow herb* - the latter presumably from its outward appearance with plants having flowers on long flowering stems.

Culpeper calls it *grass Polly* and gives the plant a variety of herbal uses. These include applying the plant's juices to the eye for eye problems such as blows to the eyes. When mixed with eye-bright (q.v.) and taken internally will help preserve good eyesight. Culpeper also claims that the plant is good for treating blindness. When made in to an ointment Culpeper claims that ulcers will heal up when treated with the ointment. Taken as a gargle the plant will "cure" quinsy and the King's evil. The water of the plant applied to the skin removes blemishes from them.

Gerard says that smoke from the burning herb drives away insects from the house – and will also drive serpents from the home.

Purple-loosestrife is describes by Allen and Hatfield as being used for treating diarrhoea in some areas.

In some areas – particularly New Zealand and North America, the plant has become invasive and threatens the local flora. Weavils and leaf beetles have been used to help control it.

HIMALAYAN (INDIAN) BALSAM

Impatiens granduliflora: *Balsaminaceae*

The plant: a glorious riverside and streamside plant. Grows to two metres in the U.K. but in the Western Himalayas, from whence it came, the plant can reach over three m. Looks stately and majestic with its cluster of pinkish-purple flowers and reddened stems. However it is also a rampant plant and can grow and spread rapidly damaging native plants on the way. This specimen was photographed on a stream edge in my garden – but only a few hundred yards away is the River Tyne where it is very much in the dominance.

The flowers: are pink-purplish in colour – and up to three or four cm in length. There is a small spur on them. The flowers grow on stalks in clusters, and are most commonly seen from July through to September or even early October. The seeds are contained in a club-shaped pod which scatters the seeds by bursting open and scattering them far and wide.

The leaves: these are pointed ovals in shape and arranged either in opposite pairs or in small whorls of three – both arrangements are shown here.

Names, mythology, uses and folk-lore

It is difficult finding colloquial names for this plant – at least those published. One I have found is jumping jack. This plant was first introduced to the U.K.in the 19th Century and within fifteen years had escaped from the gardens within which it was planted to nearby river edges. The sudden explosive release of the seeds leads to its easy spread.

The plant is on a list of invasive plants – schedule 9 of the Wildlife and Country-side act makes it illegal to plant it or encourage it to grow. In my garden edges I pull up the plants – it is an annual and its root structure very superficial. I try to do this before the seeds form – however there are many more plants upstream and their seed in part seems to be conducted down-stream to me. Although glorious in appearance it is a real pest and I suspect that there are more colloquial names out there which concisely describe the menace – but perhaps not printable here.

GOLDEN SAXIFRAGE

Chrysosplenium alternifolium and c. oppositifolium: *Saxifrageaceae*

The plants: These two plants are virtually the same – the only readily identifiable difference is the positioning of the leaves. In the one plant they are in opposite pairs on the stems and in the other they grow alternately from the stem. They are a relatively low lying plant growing to about twenty cm and both inhabit damp woodland areas predominantly. The leaves can be quite large compared with the height of the plant. They are both relatively common particularly in northern areas and the west of the country. They are quite sparse in the south.

The flowers: are small and average about five mm across, with the alternate leaved plant's flowers being slightly larger than the opposite paired leaves plant. The flowers lack petals and are greeny yellow in colour. The plants are in flower from early spring to July. They are perennials.

The leaves: both plants have similar leaves.

Names, mythology, uses and folk-lore

Names such as *creeping Jenny* and *buttered eggs* are given to this yellow-green plant. The plant can be eaten – usually in a salad or as a lightly boiled vegetable. As a herb the plant is said to have been of value in treating kidney diseases.

North York Moors near Whitby

GRASS OF PARNASSUS

Parnassia palustris: *Saxifrageaceae*

The plant: Not a grass but a hairless perennial plant of mainly damp places – grassland, moors and sometimes marshy areas. It grows to about twenty cm. Flowers from June to September and when seen there may be many plants growing – it is locally common in the north of the country but virtually absent further south. The plant is hairless. It is the county flower of Cumbria.

The flowers: about fifteen mm in diameter and have five delicate white petals, butter cup shaped, the petals having green veins on them, which can be seen in the photograph. There is one flower per stem.

The leaves: the leaves are basal and seem to clasp the flowering stem – but they are stalked.

Names, mythology, uses and folk-lore

The flower is beautiful with its delicately veining. Some say that the veins are grass-like and that these contribute to the aetiology of its name as a grass. More likely that the plant was called the Grass of Parnassus because it had been noted that cattle seemed to thrive where the flower was plentiful. They seemed to eat it preferentially. That was on Mount Parnassus in Greece.

The plant was first described in the U.K.. according to what I have been able to glean by a Flemish botanist with the name of l'Obel who saw it growing in Oxfordshire. Gerard called it White Liverwort for it was described as the liver flower of Parnassus – but I cannot give any citations for this. Gerard suggested that the leaves, in a decoction, settle down stomachs if they are drunk after being boiled in wine; the leaves will break up kidney stones.

Very few uses have been ascribed to the plant despite its great and delicate beauty – something of a surprise.

AGRIMONY

Agrimonia eupitoria – *Rosaceae*

The plant: A quite common plant growing in any grassy place. Seen in hedgerows and on those road-side verges which are not cut. This particular plant was flowering in South Close field, in Riding Mill, a Northumberland Wildlife Trust reserve. It rarely grows beyond about fifty cm in the U.K. although is said to grow to one metre on the Canadian prairies. The plant is a perennial. Agrimony is much less common in Scotland than England.

The flowers: They emerge singly from a long upright stem, and there can be many on each stem. The flowers are up to eight mm across and have five yellow petals

The leaves: Usually there are up to about six pairs of toothed and oval shaped leaves, seen particularly down the plant with smaller leaves seen between the larger ones.

Names, mythology, uses and folk-lore

The names are many and varied and there seems to be no common theme to them. An old name in Durham was *rats' tails*, and in Somerset they were known as *church steeples. Fairy's wand* crops up in different parts of the country, presumably reflecting the shape of the flower stems, and *money-in-both-pockets*. In France it was known as *Herb de St Guillaume* – a knight of Charlemagne. Another common name is Aaron's Rods.

Some of its herbal uses have been for colds and sore throats. It is said to make a quite pleasant tea (the plant is rich in tannins), and it is said also to be good for urinary infections. A regularly reported use has been for liver disease when taken in the form of a tea. In her book Lady Wilkinson says that children have been given a lot of it and seem to be neither better nor worse as a result! She states that Galen was the first to use it for liver problems (Galen was a second century A.D. Roman physician). Dioscorides, a 1st Century Greek physician, described in his De Materia Medica books, that agrimony could be used for snake bites, dysentery and liver disease. Anglo-Saxon herbalists mixed agrimony with bistort, and plantain to make an ointment for treating snake bites. The Anglo-Saxons also made a Holy Salve (ointment) of it against goblins, evils and poisons!

There are described uses for it in what is probably known today as irritable bowel syndrome – and putting the plant under the pillow would lull one off to sleep. The downside of this use for the flower is that one would not waken until it was removed!

Lady Wilkinson suggested a recipe for it – one that contained the plant, pounded frogs and human blood – for use in asthma, bronchitis, weakness of the stomach, agues, moth inflammation and haemorrhages! She describes also that the roots, when taken in an infusion with honey, or the leaves mixed in whey, could be used as a diet drink. It is good, in my opinion, to be alive today rather than in the good Lady's time!

Culpeper was not going to be left out. He described uses for the plant in treating bruises and wounds when applied topically, and it was effective against gout. The leaves and seeds taken in wine could be used for the bloody flux (dysentry).

Agrimony has also been used in wool dyes.

Its name may be derived from its usefulness to treat eye disease known in Greek as argema.

The Bible refers to the plant in Numbers 17, verses 1-3, as "gathering rods" identifying the tribes of Israel. *'And the Lord spoke to Moses, saying: "Speak to the children of Israel, and get from them a rod from each father's house, all their leaders according to their fathers' houses; twelve rods. Write each man's name on his rod. And you shall write Aaron's name on the rod of Levi. For there shall be one rod for the head of each father's house."'*

BARREN STRAWBERRY

Potentilla sterilis: *Rosaceae*

The plant: like the wild strawberry it grows well in dry places, but also in woodland areas. It is a perennial and spreads through runners which root. Usually smaller than the strawberry – probably nearer to twelve cm tall.

The flowers: five petalled but the petals seem usually to be more widely separated than the than the true strawberry flowers. Are about ten to fifteen mm across. Flower earlier than the strawberry – but the flowering season does overlap (from March to June). The flowers are white.

The leaves: like the fragaria (strawberry) these are essentially oval and tri-foliate and are toothed. The terminal tooth is ***shorter*** than the adjacent ones and this distinguishes it from the strawberry.

Names, mythology, uses and folk-lore

The colloquial names include *lazy bones* and *strawberry plant* both of which are said by Grigson to come from the south-west of England. The herbalists largely ignore the plant as being a separate one from the whole Fragaria family.

Gerard mentions it as a *wilde Strawberry* which is entirely devoid of any fruit. He does describe one or two uses for the plants but does not distinguish the barren strawberry from any other in this regard.

Culpeper also describes uses for all the strawberry plants. The juices from the leaves and roots derived from boiling them are said to cure loose teeth and spongy gums – but the list of uses of strawberry leaves given by Culpeper includes the treatment of jaundice, wound healing, panting and beating of the heart, sore mouths, inflamed eyes, bloody courses of women, and for many inflammations.

Gerard describes the water after being distilled following boiling with the leaves, and drunk with white wine, is good against *passion of the heart, and for reviving the spirits and making the heart merry!*

Grigson describes the plant as ...*the small and charming liar of the spring, posing as a strawberry*. A good way to remember it!

BURNET ROSE

Rosa pimpinellifolia: *Rosaceae*

The plant: The Burnet rose is a shrub which extends by suckers. The stems are particularly thorny. It is generally found on sand dunes and this particular plant was found on the dunes at Seaton Sluice in Northumberland.

The flowers: As with many roses they appear in the May to July period and are three to five cm in diameter. The petals themselves are white or creamy white and the flowers are usually solitary. As with all roses the petals are five in number. The fruit of the Burnet rose is purple/black when ripe.

The leaves: The leaves are quite characteristic with approximately nine to eleven oval leaflets.

Names, mythology, uses and folk-lore

The Burnet rose is seen throughout the United Kingdom but is only common in localised areas. In Seaton Sluice, for example, there are many Burnet rose bushes but further north and further south on the sand the plant may not appear at all. Its height varies. Some plants are quite small reaching only twenty to thirty cm. Other plants can be over a metre in height. This is a rose that is native to much of Europe going as far north as Norway and Iceland. It can be seen also in North Africa, particularly towards the west.

Grigson gives only a few lines to the Burnet rose and describes how Gerard was the first herbalist to describe it. The Burnet rose is also unusual in that it produces black fruits rather than the scarlet red coloured hips more commonly associated with roses. The name of the Burnet rose derives from Gerard: he described the leaves as like those of the salad Burnet which is a perennial of chalk grassland. I can find no reliable reference to this rose having any culinary or herbal uses although it has been used in rose breeding. The Burnet rose is arguably one of the most aromatic of the wild roses in the UK.

COMMON DOG ROSE

Rosa canina: *Rosaceae*

The plant: This is a delightful plant of summer time, its flowers coming out in late May or early June. It is a climbing plant and it can reach three m or more in height, particularly when growing through and up hedges.

The flowers: The flowers are usually at least five cm across and sometimes much more. Usually it is pink with yellow stamens. The flowers themselves have five petals, each lobed and usually there are up to four flowers at the end of each stem.

The leaves: The leaves are glossy and ovoid. The stems are thorny. The plant pictured here was photographed in June in Upper Weardale.

Names, mythology, uses and folk-lore

The dog rose is a very common plant seen throughout much of the UK although much less commonly so in the northern areas of Scotland. It is mentioned in the Song of Solomon in the Bible where in Chapter 2, verse 1, there is a description given of "*I am a rose over Sharon*". The Virgin Mary is often depicted with a rose but when that is the case the rose will not have thorns.

A blood-red rose is also a symbol of martyrdom and the white rose a symbol of purity. As well as being called dog rose other colloquial names include *briar rose, choop rose, liars* and *dyke-rose* – although this is usually a reference to the hedge rose.

The fruits of the rose are called hips and these are given a large variety of regional names, including *pig's noses, nipper nails, dog jobs, choops* and *hippens.* Grigson, in reviewing the history of the dog rose states that the wild rose i.e. the dog rose, was much less used in medical cases than garden roses and Gerard refers to the dog rose to distinguish it from the garden rose which he clearly favoured, indicating that in his garden he had all types of rose except the briar bush which he thought unworthy to be placed in the garden. Culpeper can usually be relied upon to describe uses for plants but with the rose he begins his description by saying "*What a pother have authors made with the roses! What a racket have they kept?*" He then goes on to describe the rose over the next three pages. He describes a huge variety of uses for the rose – for example he says that "*the decoction of red roses made with wine and used is very good for the headache, and pains in the eyes, ears, throat and gums; as also for.......the lower part of the belly and the matrix* being bathed or put into them. The same decoction of the roses remaining in it is profitably applied to the region of the heart to ease the inflammation therein.*" He also goes on to describe its use in St Anthony's Fire and diseases of the stomach.

* the meaning of this is uncertain to me

It could stay women's courses and the red roses, presumably the garden roses, could strengthen the heart, the stomach, the liver and "*the retentive faculty*". The rose also mitigated the pains that arise from heat, from inflammation, and that they could procure rest and sleep as well as staying both whites and reds in women, and useful for gonorrhoea, all running of the veins and fluxes of the belly. Its range of uses is enormous from Culpeper's description. Almost certainly, given such a wide range of use, it was probably of little value in any of them.

However one remembers as a child being encouraged by school teachers to collect rosehips. These were taken in large quantity in the early autumn to the teacher who would then bag them all up in the school and the school would sell them to companies which made rosehip syrup – a mixture rich in vitamin C and used to try and prevent winter ailments such as colds and fever. Rose oil is also the basis of many perfumes. There are other common roses to look out for – these include the **field rose** which has a white flower and grows to about a height of one metre as a shrub but the stems are trailing and these plants are associated with woodland margins, hedgerows and scrub. Another common rose is the **sweet briar** which grows up to three m in height but has relatively small pink flowers. The flowers are a much deeper pink than those of the dog rose. Another common rose is the **Japanese rose**. This is a purple-pink flowered rose growing to well over a metre in height. It is a shrub and is planted but has also become naturalised. The Japanese rose is quite common throughout most of England, although largely absent from the north of Scotland. With the exception of the Japanese rose, these roses are all naturally occurring in the British Isles.

CREEPING CINQUEFOIL

Potentilla reptans: *Rosaceae*

The plant: a common creeping plant found in any grassland and especially in my experience on road-side verges as was this plant photographed near Riding Mill in Northumberland. It is a common plant never appearing more than about twenty cm in height. Its runners root at nodes on the stem, like strawberries, and form a new plant. The plant is a perennial.

The flowers: five petals and very striking. These flowers appear in mid-summer from June onwards. The petals are lobed on their outermost surface.

The leaves: are long and stalked – and are hairless.

Names, mythology, uses and folk-lore

The names *five fingers* and *five finger grass* seem to be commonly quoted.

Gerard says that a decoction of the herb held in the mouth cured tooth-ache. Culpeper gave it a variety of uses including the root being valuable against all fluxes and bleeding. It helped diseases of the liver and lungs, helped putrefying ulcers of the mouth, with vinegar it would be good against shingles and would "*appease the rage of any fretting sores*".

Grigson delves deeply in to the folk-lore surrounding the plant. He refers to an ointment allegedly used by witches which included the fat of children dug from their graves, of the juice of *smallage, wolfbane* and *cinquefoil,* mingled with *the meal of fine wheat.* He does not disclose the uses this mixture was applied to and I have been unable to go back to the source he used for this information (Bacon: 1627; Sylva sylvarum).

In the old herbals cinquefoils seem to relate to all cinquefoils rather than to specific plants. Some of the other flowers include ***hoary, sulphur, shrubby*** and ***marsh*** although the only one reasonably common one in the north of England is ***marsh cinquefoil.***

LADY'S MANTLE

Alchemilla vulgaris: *Rosaceae*

The plant: a perennial usually seen in grassland and meadows – but some varieties are garden plants. Grows to about thirty cm.

Flowers: these are tiny being only two mm or so across. They are clustered at the top of the plant and are yellow-green in colour. Easy to confuse these flowers with lady's bedstraw although this latter plant has four clearly separate petals. Flowers throughout the summer.

The leaves: these are lobed but overall circular in outline. They are of varying size from a few cm to many. They are stalked.

Names, mythology, uses and folk-lore

There are few colloquial names but those which are, or have been, used relate to the plant's ability to sustain dew drops on their upper surface – for example *dew-cup*. Other names may relate to their shape – *lion's foot, bear's foot* and *duck's foot*.

This is a plant present in many modern herbals where it is listed as curing excessive menstruation. The plant juice is also described as curing acne. There are also repeated references to the leaves inducing sleepiness if they are placed under the pillow.

Grigson describes the plant as a plant of old northern magic - because of the dew drops which accumulate in the leaves and also the shape of the leaves with, usually, nine lobes. He also describes it being associated with magic elves in curing cows after they had previously been shot by elves and were now sick.

Culpeper describes its use in treating inflamed wounds, and also for stopping bleeding, vomiting, fluxes of all sorts, bruises, ruptures and was also useful in treating women suffering symptoms from large breasts. It can cure all green wounds and old sores even if they were fistulous or hollow. Distilled water from the plant aided conception and increased the chances of a live baby.

Pechey also continued the theme of treating rupture – he specifically mentions it as being useful for children with "bursten bellies". I am not certain what he means by this – it could be a ventral hernia, or it could even be exomphalos when the child is born without a complete abdominal wall and there is an open hernia present at birth. Pechey then gives a medicine recipe for treating fluxes:

- Lady's mantle
- Sanicle
- Golden rod
- Sengreen
- Betony
- Agrimony – all these one handful each
- Marshmallow – two handsful
- Fern
- Camomile
- St John's Wort
- Mugwort
- Briars

- Origanum
- Tormentil leaves and roots – all one handful each
- Mix and put in three bags and boil them in ("faeces of") red wine!

Who did the study to show that this recipe was the best for these conditions? Was each item paid for separately? Pechey gives no clue to the answer(s).

Dunstanburgh castle, Craster, Northumberland

MEADOWSWEET

Filipendula ulmaria: *Rosaceae*

The plant: a common shrubby plant in the whole country – U.K. that is – seen best in damp areas – damp meadows, marshes, ditches and by the side of streams. Grows to about 1.5 metres. It is a perennial and often is present in large swathes of the plant giving it an almost shrubby look.

The flowers: each is small – about six mm in diameter but are carried in large sprays. They are fragrant and just off-white in colour. Present through most of the summer.

The leaves: these are roughly oval in shape and are quite difficult to show in a photograph for the plant is quite dense. The leaves are in pairs with smaller leaflets between them.

Names, mythology, uses and folk-lore

The plant is one of the most written about that I have come across. There are numerous reference to the following names by which it can be called: *Queen of the meadow, pride of the meadow, dropwort, bride wort, petite rein, lady of the meadow* and so on.

The plant is described as having a pleasant taste and it certainly has a pleasant odour. This made it valuable as a plant to be scattered about houses and churches, but mainly on the floors, to impart a warm sensation underfoot and to create a pleasing aroma about the house. It is said to have been Queen Elizabeth 1's favourite herb when used in this way. The name bride wort comes from its use in churches at weddings for just these purposes.

The whole plant can be eaten and it is said to be good for treating gastritis and it can also be used in pot-pourri arrangements. Chewing the roots is claimed to cure headaches – the plant contains salicylic acid, which is aspirin. The plant also contains tannins and these are claimed to have an anti-inflammatory effect in the plant when taken, and an effect that reduces mucus production.

Has been used in modern times to treat colds, bronchitis, upset stomachs, heartburn, stomach ulcers and joint disorders. The plant is said to act as a diuretic.

Gerard said that the flowers boiled in wine and drunk resulted in a "merrie heart". Distilled water from the flowers dropped to the eyes would take any bruising and itching away.

The plant juices, when mixed with copper, provide a black dye.

Pechey described the plant as being useful in treating those who spit blood.

An interesting ancient Welsh legend is related to Gwydion and Math who created out of oak blossom, broom and meadowsweet a woman. She was named *Blodeuwedd.* There are many internet web sites which detail this very complicated story, but which are well worth consulting!

PIRI-PIRI-BUR

Acaena novae-zelandiae: *Rosaceae*

The plant: is a creeping perennial plant which colonizes dry and sandy places. It grows to about fifteen cm. in height.

The flowers: are tiny, white and difficult to see. However, the fruits are burs and these are very evident. They stick to almost any clothing and even to shoe laces – and thus can spread very widely. The plant can become invasive in no time at all.

The leaves: are almost inconsequential in the presence of the burs – they are divided into several pairs of leaflets for each plant.

Names, mythology, uses and folk-lore

The plant is, very sadly, a menace. It was brought in to the country from New Zealand on sheep fleeces, but is now widely established in sandy areas and coastal sites in East Anglia and also on Holy Island. The BBC has a web page on its Earth News site which describes the plant as being – potentially – critically invasive and that banning the sale of the plant is probably the best form of control. Even so, any visitor to the areas where the plant has become established, should take great care to ensure that there are no burs or seeds attaching to their clothing before leaving the site.

I can find no herbal uses for the plant – but I include it in this book to warn of its aggressive invasiveness.

SILVERWEED

Potentilla anserina – *Rosaceae*

The plant: A very common and readily seen plant. It is low growing and is often seen on road-side verges where the draught from passing vehicles blows the leaves and shows the silver under-surface. More often seen in damp places, but also on bare ground as well as meadow and grassland.

The flowers: bright yellow with five petals and up to two cm in diameter, although often smaller. Flowers from May to August/September.

The leaves: each comprises up to about twelve leaflets. They are covered by a silvery hair that gives the plant its name.

Names, mythology, uses and folk-lore

This is a very common plant and one of its main uses has been as a food – especially when other supplies, such as potatoes, are scarce. The boiled roots are a substitute and were used in centuries past as potatoes are used now. The taste is said to be reminiscent of parsnip.

The plants have been used against mouth ulcers, stones, internal wounds and wounds of the privy parts according to the older herbalists. The plant is also used to cleanse the skin of spots and blemishes and has been used in this way from the sixteenth century up to the present time. It has been used to heal the blemishes left by smallpox. A small leaf of the plant placed inside the shoe is said to stop excessive foot sweating and this use went on for centuries until the mid-twentieth century. Grigson says that this was first described by Deering in 1738. Two of the plant's colloquial names are *travellers' joy* and *chafe grass*.

Other names that seem to be frequently assigned to the plant are *silver fern, tansy, moss-corns, silver grass, silver feather* and *bread and butter*.

An internet search of silverweed became a little confusing when web sites refer to the plant *Argentina anserine* being the *common silverweed* or *silverweed cinquefoil* – or just *silverweed*. The accompanying photographs on the Wikipedia site show plants identical to *potentilla anserina*. I can find no botanical reference to Argentina anserina, including a search of Flora Britannica.

A nice legend quoted on the Wikipedia site is that of Jesus walking along the dusty roads and the plants at the side of the road being these, with yellow flowers, becoming known as *Footsteps of our Lord*.

TORMENTIL

Potentilla erecta: *Rosaceae*

The plant: This is a low-lying creeping, perennial which flourishes on heaths and moors. It is common on the Pennine hills. Can also be seen in grasslands. It can grow to about thirty cm. but rarely have I seen it at that 'great' height.

The flowers: Bright yellow, and about one cm in diameter, there are four petals each being gently notched on its most lateral margin in each flower. The flowers arise singly from a slender stem. They can be seen all summer long.

The leaves: are trifoliate.

Names, mythology, uses and folk-lore

Grigson cites many local names for tormentil and these include *blood root, ewe daisy*, and *shepherd's knot* which I have heard and which are cited in various other descriptions. Another name is *English sarsaparilla*.

It has been used for intestinal problems. If three desert-spoonfuls are boiled in water and then drunk diarrhoea can be cured. The roots are said to "stimulate" the immune system. Another recipe is to boil the roots in milk and this will settle loose bowels in children when given to the child.

The name tormentil is derived from its properties in treating colic – *tormina* is Latin for colic and tormentil torments colic – thus eradicating it.

The roots are highly astringent and fishermen in the Scottish regions have been known to tan their nets by using the roots.

Gerard describes it as curative of diarrhoea and the *bloody flux* if it is presented to the patient in water that has been used to quench hot steel. Gerard, too, gives it some herbal uses, including "curing" the heart, expelling poisons and provoking sweats.

The roots are the main ingredient of an American agent for stopping diarrhoea in children and then rehydrating them (Quicklyte®, Lev Laboratories). The roots are also the main ingredient of a Bavarian and Black Forest liqueur – Penninger Blutwurz.

WATER AVEN

Geum rivale: *Rosaceae*

The plant: a lovely plant of damp areas such as field-side ditches and damp grassland. It is downy. The plant shown here was photographed in a road-side ditch in upper Weardale. It can grow to fifty cm, or sometimes more especially if near trees. It is a perennial.

The flowers: are pendulant and bell shaped. The petals are basically pink, but surrounded by dark red sepals. The seed pods are quite characteristic – they resemble burs – a bit like the burdock plants – but they are soft and feathery. Flower in much of the summer from May until well into the autumn.

The leaves: for the most part these are trifoliate except those at the base of the plant where they are pinnate. At the base the leaves can be difficult to see due to the usually dense foliage cover from other plants such as grass.

Names, mythology, uses and folk-lore

One of the commonest names given to the plant colloquially is *granny's bonnet* although other plants are sometimes given the same name. Although it is a common plant in areas where it is seen, one can spend many hours fruitlessly looking for it – it is best described as locally common throughout the U.K. although less common in the south of the country.

Surprisingly in my opinion, for such a striking plant, it seems to have very few uses in the herbalists' pharmacopoeia. The only use I can find is the dried roots may protect against moth infestations in clothing.

WILD STRAWBERRY

Fragaria vesca: *Rosaceae*

The plant: Found in grassy place – prefers dry conditions – and on the waysides by paths. Grows by putting out runners which themselves may root. Never more than twenty five cm or so tall – but usually much smaller. Is a perennial. The plant is virtually identical to the *barren strawberry*: the distinguishing feature is the size of the terminal tooth on the leaf - on the strawberry this is usually ***longer*** than the adjacent ones as shown on the picture insert.

The flowers: these are five-petalled and about twelve to fifteen mm across. Usually seen between April and July. They are replaced by fruits – tiny strawberries which are usually beautifully flavoured. A great find on any walk!

The leaves: they are basically oval, but toothed, and are comprised of three leaflets. They are hairy underneath. The terminal tooth stands out from the others.

Names, mythology, uses and folk-lore

Apart from the obvious use of the strawberry as a food few other uses are attributed to the plant. Allen and Hatfield describe that the leaves, when rubbed on the face, can improve the complexion, a property implemented by some Cornish women in the past. Wild strawberries were sometimes collected by children to be sold at market – but to pick a sufficient number for this would have been a very labour intensive exercise. Herbal teas made from the wild strawberry were claimed to control diarrhoea. The strawberry is shown in a triptych painting from the sixteenth strawberry by Hieronymus Bosch – *The Garden of Earthly Delights* and an account of this is summarised in Wikipedia. It is suggested that the painting was initially commissioned as an altar painting: this does seem improbable given the rather extensive use of the strawberry fruit, in the middle panel especially, showing some erotic images! Whatever you may feel about the strawberry in the wild it is a great bonus to be able to pick a handful and enjoy them in a pause on a country walk.

The origin of the name is much debated – Grigson carries an account of this suggesting that it might have been given by gardeners who protect the garden variety of fruit by putting straw around the plants. You must contemplate whether this is plausible or not!

WOOD AVEN

Geum urbanum: *Rosaceae*

The plant: A very common plant which most people see and simply walk on by. It is a perennial and, like its cousin the water aven, it is downy. The plant grows to about fifty cm. Seen, as the name suggests, in woodland but also in hedges. If the plant is seen in the vicinity of water avens cross hybridisation may occur.

The flowers: The flowers are seen from May until early autumn. There are five yellow petals and five green sepals a little longer than the petals. The fruits are like burs, similar to the water aven, but the spikes are hooked and more rigid and cling, for example, to fur of animals and can thus be spread around. This is a hermaphrodite flower, pollination being by bees.

The leaves: are often over-looked. At the base of the plant they have up to six side leaflets and a terminal one that appears much larger. The stem leaves are three lobed. They are all green.

Names, mythology, uses and folk-lore

Has been widely known as *Herb Bennet.* Also widely known as the *blessed herb* which comes from the old French word *benoite* the modern equivalent being *bénit* which, translated, means *consecrated* or *holy.* In the thirteenth century the plant was often depicted in the stone work of Church buildings: this is said to be due to the association of the plant with Christ in the leaves, which are three lobed and therefore reminiscent of the Holy Trinity and the flower has five petals, which are reflective of the Five Wounds of Christ – one in each hand and foot with the fifth being the abdominal wound inflicted by the Roman soldier when he was on the cross. The plant is said to have the power to drive away evil spirits, including the devil, and is effective at protecting against the bites of rabid dogs!

In complete contrast to its near relative, the water aven, this plant has numerous uses attributed to it – especially by Culpeper. I simply list some of them: diseases of the chest and breasts, pains and stitches in the side and expels crude raw humours from the belly and stomach. In addition it is effective at dissolving congealed blood following falls, and the roots boiled in wine cured a large range of internal diseases – it strengthened the heart and also the *cold brain* (I have no idea what is meant by this – but possibly it refers to migraine).

In the spring the roots can cure obstructions of the liver, and help those with ruptures. The plant can take away facial spots. Steeping the roots in wine in spring, said Culpeper, will provide a pleasant drink that would be a preservative against the plague and any other poison. He concluded by stating that it is a very safe herb and was fit to be kept in everybody's house.

The plant is still recommended by some as being a good mouthwash for the management of halitosis. Parts of the plant have also been used as a spice and in flavouring ales.

The roots smell of cloves and the dried roots placed in the clothes cupboard would prevent any moth attacks.

A remarkable plant which has properties which, if true and tested, would replace a large proportion of all modern drugs. You can come to your own judgement on why it has not done so! It has been grown as a garden plant in the past – beware of doing this for it can take over the garden!

ST JOHN'S WORT (HAIRY)

Hypericum hirsutum: *Clusiaceae*

The plant: this common variety of the St John's wort family is the representative of this group of plants of which there are about nine or so species which may be found in the U.K. The plant is well known for its herbal properties and this use of the plant seems to be especially common. Some of the plants of St John's wort are relatively common but even the so-called common plants are often described as being widespread but only locally common. The plant shown here was photographed in Upper Teesdale on a stream embankment (approximate map ref: 847307) and this is the only St John's Wort I have come across in the areas used for the plant photography. The stream was on a heath, high in the Dale. The plant was about sixty cm high but it can be taller in more favourable environments. The plant is a perennial.

The flowers: these are one of the main distinguishing features of the plant. The flowers at first sight look little different from plants such as agrimony and golden rod. However, the flowers here show some dark red markings on the edge of some of the five petals: these are small and easily missed. There are also gland-like structure arising from the edge of the smaller pointed sepals; these "glands" are stalked. The petal markings, small red markings at the edge of the petal, are shown in the photograph of the flower petals and the glands on the sepals can be seen quite easily on the edges of the sepals. The plant flowers from June to early September.

The leaves: are ovoid in shape and have well-marked veins and, in addition, have pale markings, not always easy to see, which are usually described as translucent spots. They can be seen in the original photograph but are less distinct on the prints from it. Look carefully, perhaps with a magnifying glass, to spot them.

Names, mythology, uses and folk-lore

This is a well-known herbal plant – very few people are likely to be ignorant of the plant. It is a plant that can reproduce both sexually and vegetatively. It tends not to grow above about five thousand feet (about fifteen hundred metres) - and it tends to do badly in dry areas and in cool areas when low temperatures might prevent the seed germinating. However it is a perennial plant so should grow on last year's root stock.

Where it does grow it can become invasive and there are also some reports which suggest that it is poisonous to cattle – so spread of the plant into cattle-grazing areas may cause problems. In some parts, beetles have been bred which live on the plant and thus destroy it.

Its dominant medical use has been in controlling the symptoms of depression and it is claimed that it has an efficacy similar to conventional anti-depressants. I have been unable to access an article which is said to confirm this – but the citation site for the article is given at the end of this account.[1]

It is a herb which has a strong association with legends – and with magic. The St John in the name is of John the Baptist. John was the cousin of Jesus and, on the order of King Herod, he was beheaded (Matthew 14:1-12). John's death is commemorated on August 29th. The red spots on the petals are "representative" of John's spilled blood, and the translucent leaf spots reflect tears shed at the news of his death. There are many, sometimes quite confusing, legends written up on this.

The herb has long been held to be obnoxious to evil spirits. Herbs were picked before sunrise on June 23rd, when they had dew on them (dew itself is claimed by many to be magical) and then burned in the evening. Taking in the smoke was purifying to the person. Jumping over the fire had the same effect. (One has seen Buddhist traditions of running through flames and smoke – but not from St John's Wort – to achieve purification).

Other legends say that if the herb is picked on mid-summer's eve, that fertility would be improved. Country girls would pick the herb, hang it over their doors, and sleep with it under the pillow; it would not only get rid of evil spells, but could also inform the girl who her future husband might be.

Other legends suggest that when the herb has been picked for the celebration, but left over and simply allowed to die, would be associated with death occurring. The herb also protected against money spells and gave good health and happiness. It also protected against lightning and house fires especially when the herb was burnt indoors and the smoke allowed to perfuse through all the rooms.

Christianity adopted some of the customs associated with the herb – St John's Day is June 24th – six months before Christmas Day celebrating the birth of Christ. This mid-summer festival linked the plant with St John – the plant had bright yellow flowers and a red juice, which could link it with the beheading.

However it is suggested that the herb had its magic properties long before it became associated with St John.

The herb's name in Wales is Ysgol Christ (in this context Ysgol means ladder) – Christ's ladder. (Grigson).

The plant is also associated with St Columba who carried some with him as protection. If found by accident, the plant was then said to display its magical properties. Conversely it was believed that if the plant was stood on, elves would cause the plant's assailant a sleepless night.

What is written here is but a small proportion of what can be found on the internet and in books – have a good time searching, but do not believe all you read!

Modern herbals have given plenty of room in the books for this herb. It has a variety of uses described by different books but include treating: depression, nervous disorders, stomach and gut problems, bed wetting and (used externally) to enhance wound healing.

The internet is also full of advertisements for pills of St John's wort. Always be wary of what you buy should you feel the (ill-advised, in my opinion) need to buy on the internet. Modern high-street stores are probably a safer bet for purchasing the herb There is a steady trickle of reports of St John's wort overdoses in the press.

A good plant identifier should show the other St John's wort plants which may be seen. These might include ***perforate or imperforate St John's worts, slender St John's wort*** and ***trailing St John's wort.*** Others are less common.

1 Berner LK, Kriston, L
St John's wort for major depression.
Cochrane Database of Systemic Reviews 2008, Issue 4, Art number CD00044g

POPPY:

Papaver dubium and rhoeas: *Papaveraceae*

The plant: This grows typically on disturbed ground and arable land. It grows to about sixty cm. or so and is often seen in summer corn fields where it contrasts with the corn. It is also a plant of the way-side and road-side. The red poppy here was growing on the edge of a field of oil-seed rape near Corbridge in Northumberland.

The flowers: they are generally described by folk as being a deep scarlet red – but closer inspection shows them often to be more of an orange-red colour. However you might describe them they are truly vivid in appearance. The flower heads are usually about six cm in diameter and there are four overlapping petals which feel quite papery to the touch. The poppy shown is the ***long-headed poppy*** and has no dark blotches at the base of the flower which so characterises the other, or ***common poppy*** in the second insert (papaver rhoeas). Otherwise there is little to distinguish one from the other. The common poppy is, ironically, less common in the north of England and Scotland than the long-headed poppy shown here. The flowers are relatively short lived, appearing usually in

June, and when they die off the flowers leave a quite characteristic seed head which can be a quite elongated capsule. The other poppy shown is the yellow poppy, or Welsh poppy – a successful garden escapee.

The leaves: these are similar between both the long-headed and common varieties being quite slender and divided.

Names, mythology, uses and folk-lore

These comments relate to all the red poppies (see below). Grigson presents some interesting observation on the poppy – he says that its presence in corn-fields goes back for millennia, citing the fact it used to be the farmers inseparable companion in the corn fields. The Roman Goddess Ceres, Goddess of the earth and, therefore, cultivation, was usually depicted in art work and on coins clutching poppies in one hand and corn in the other – the association between corn and poppies being so strong even then. The poppy plant and its hypnotic qualities were well known in the classical period of ancient Greece and are mentioned by contemporary writers. It was regarded as a magic or poisonous plant and was used in religious ceremonies. At a later date it was also employed in the art of healing. The serum which exudes from a cut poppy was given the name Aphrodite's tears shed at the loss of her beloved Adonis.

The red poppies in the U.K. do contain opium - but in much smaller amounts than the papaver somniferum from which opium is usually extracted. In Victorian times there was a trade in opium from the northern European plants but oriental opium became so easily, and so cheaply, available that production of opium in this country ceased.

Grigson refers to the opium poppy being known by Neolithic peoples in the lake-side villages of Switzerland. Some improbable folk-lore traditions are associated with it – picking the flower brings on thunder – but poppies placed under the roof timbers protected the buildings from lightning. Quite how these opposite effects could be observed, or attributed, to the poppy, is beyond me – but if you know the answer do please let me know! The poppy – and probably the northern poppy rather than the somniferum variety - was used to calm babies when teething, and poppy tea was used to treat fevers and rheumatism (Allen and Hatfield). Opium from the northern plant was probably the one used when opium began to replace gin for treating teething pains!(Allen and Hatfield). Allen and Hatfield also list a number of other uses for the wild poppy – including chewing the poppy heads to treat headaches (that is, the hangover variety!).

Note: there are four red poppies described – ***rough poppy*** and ***prickly poppy*** in addition to those described here – but these are becoming rare even in the South of England which is more their natural habitat. Others include the *yellow horned-poppy* and the *Welsh poppy* and the *greater celandine* is also usually considered to be a poppy. However these three are from different genera – and the Welsh poppy is probably a garden escapee.

AUTUMN GENTIAN

Gentiana amarella: *Gentianaceae*

The plant: On balance I feel that the gentian photographed is the autumn gentian. This was pictured on Holy Island on sandy "soil". Against it being the autumn gentian is the flower colour – the autumn gentian is purple in appearance whereas this plant has a purple-cream colour to it. The close up photograph overleaf shows a very slight purple tinge which suggests this to be an autumn variety. **Gentiana campestris,** the field gentian is invariably four petalled. The solitary end-flower on the stem is also more typically the appearance of the field gentian. Field gentians occur on Holy Island to the best of my knowledge. Could this plant be a hybrid between the two or just a pale autumn variety? Your opinion would be of great interest to me.

The flower: This is five petalled and there are five calyces. The leaves are narrow and ovoid. The flowering stem is no more than about ten cm in height. The autumn gentian is usually taller – to about twenty cm. The autumn gentian has either four or five petals. Its properties are very similar to the field gentian. The autumn variety is also known as *felwort.*

Of the gentians, Culpeper describes the plants as cleansing and scouring plants which can open up obstructions. It helps the biting of venomous beasts and mad dogs. They also aid digestion and they "*cleanseth*" the body of raw humours. The roots are useful for "burst ruptures". My edition of Gerard ignores the gentians!

Allen and Hatfield describe the field gentian being used in the northern parts of Scotland as a tonic, and useful against jaundice. In Shetland it has been used for "digestive disorders". The field gentian has been used in areas where the centaury is absent (centaureum erythraea – q.v.).

COMMON CENTAURY

Centaureum erythraea: *Gentianaceae*

The plant: a relatively common plant, an annual, growing especially on sand dunes and any dry places especially where there is chalk in the soil. This plant was photographed on the cliff tops of the Durham Coastal path. Grows to about twenty cm. in height.

The flowers: these are five-petalled and in various shades of pink. The flowers photographed here were no more than ten mm. in diameter but flowers up to fifteen mm are reported. They open fully in the sun. As the picture shows the flowers are in clusters at the ends of each flowering stem and each flowering side stem.

The leaves: these are ovoid in appearance at the base of the plant but further up the stems the leaves are narrower and pointed.

Names, mythology, uses and folk-lore

Some of its names link this plant to gentians and web sites refer to this as well as Grigson. The plant was known as *gentian* in some parts because it was used in place of gentiana lutea a plant which had to be imported by herbalists and physicians. Other names include *mountain flax, blood wort*, and *sanctuary*.

It was said to be a blessed herb in that it brought good luck if brought in to the house between the Annunciation (March 25th when the Angel Gabriel announced to Mary that she would conceive in her womb and bear a son whose name would be Jesus - Luke 1:26-38) and the Assumption (August 15th commemorating the death of the Virgin Mary and her *Assumption* in to heaven). It is also said to have grown where Christ trod on his way to the cross.

Culpeper describes a number of uses for the plant. It was good for opening the stoppings of the liver, gall and spleen. It purged the humours of cholera, and he recommended it for the management of sciatica. Used outwardly it cured agues. The plant was used to kill parasitic worms, and it was effective against adder bites especially if taken in wine (one gram of the dried plant added to the wine). Used as a decoction it could kill off and clean out worms in the ears, and would also cleanse foul ulcers of the head.

Allen and Hatfield describe the plant as having been used by the Romans and they repeat the plant's quite widespread use for liver diseases.

Note: this plant might be confused with the ***dwarf centaury*** which also grows in coastal areas. It is pretty much the same in its flowers as the common centaury but does not grow nearly as tall. The plant photographed here was about twenty cm in height and I think it should be called the common centaury. There are a number of other centaury plants – but they are either rare or non-existent in the northern half of Britain. These include ***yellow centaury, lesser centaury*** and the exceedingly rare ***perennial centaury.*** Another rare centaury is one that grows only in a few places in the north of the British Isles – the ***seaside centaury.***

SEASIDE CENTAURY

Centaurium littorale: *Gentianaceae*

The plant: An uncommon plant in much of the country but is seen in the more Northern parts in coastal sites. This one was photographed growing in the dunes of Holy Island. It is a small plant, being only about ten cm tall (although some descriptions state it can grow to twenty cm). No doubt it grows elsewhere in the north-east of England in coastal dunes, but I have not seen it elsewhere. The plant is seen widely in Europe as far north as the more northern parts of Finland.

The flowers: are a bright darkish-pink colour which is almost luminescent in character. There are five petals and the flower are about eight to ten mm across. This is a flower of mid to late summer with this one being photographed in August. The flowers are unstalked and the stamens are yellow.

The leaves: towards the base of the plant the leaves are grey/yellow green with almost parallel sides: on the stem the leaves are green, fleshy and parallel sided and are only about four mm or so across.

Names, mythology, uses and folk-lore

Very little seems to be written separately about the seaside centaury from the common centaury, possibly because of its comparative rarity.

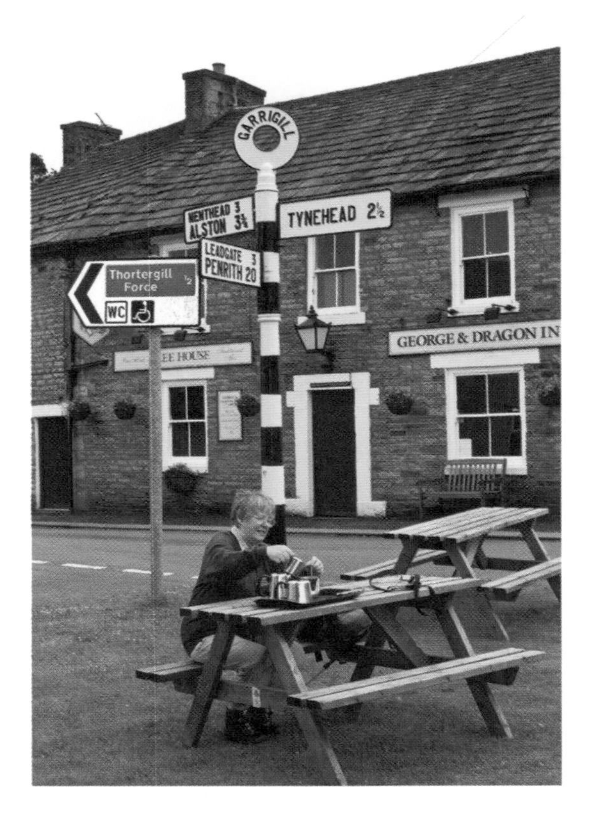

Garrigil, South Tyne – where to next?

SPRING GENTIAN

Gentiana verna – *Gentianaceae*

The plant: a small plant of only a few cm. in height. The vivid blue flowers contrast with the limestone grassland on which it grows best. Found only in Upper Teesdale – near Cow Green reservoir - in the U.K. and probably only one site in Ireland. At Cow Green the gentians flowering in June are a wonderful spectacle. Well worth the trip just to see them – and, usually, there will be many to see.

The flower: bright blue with five petals. About two cm across.

The leaves: bright green. On the stems they arise opposite one another in pairs, but in a rosette at the base.

Names, mythology, uses and folk-lore

Although exceedingly rare in the U.K. this gentian is widespread in Europe in Alpine areas up to about 2500m and can also be found in Iran, Iraq, and Turkey. Rare in the U.K. and also in the more northern parts of Europe.

A number of superstitions are linked with the plant. In Germany it is said to be unlucky to bring the flower in to the house – the individual concerned would be struck by lightning. If that person avoids the lightning strike, death would soon follow in any case.

Wikipedia lists a number of uses to which the plant has been applied – these include digestive problems, hypertension, cancer, wound healing, parasitic worms and so on. With so many disparate uses it is unlikely that it is effective against any.

It is the county flower of Durham and the national flower of Austria. The flower was featured on a postage stamp issued in 1964 in G.B. to commemorate the 10th International Botanical Congress held in Edinburgh. The Gentian's Latin name features in the eulogy of Serbian soldiers who died in the liberation of Macedonia at the end of World War 1.

Other gentians which may be seen include the marsh gentian a plant that is widely scattered but relatively rare, seen in marshy and boggy spaces. The autumn/field gentians are mentioned elsewhere in this book.

COMMON BUTTERWORT

Pinguicula vulgaris: *Lentibulariaceae*

The plant: This is an unusual plant – it is carnivorous via the sticky leaves which capture and digest insects careless enough to come too close. It is small and grows only to about twelve or so cm in height. The plant favours moist soils and even boggy areas. This one was photographed in a damp part of Holy Island. Rarely seen in the southern parts of the U.K. but commoner in the north. It is a perennial.

The flowers: these are pale blue with a white throat and are never more than about ten mm. in length. Look behind the flower and a spur of about four mm should be seen. The lower lip is lobed. Flowers are present in the earlier part of summer. There is one flower per stem.

The leaves: are arranged in a basal rosette and are yellow-green in colour giving he impression initially that the plant is dying. It will not be! The leaves are sticky and covered in hairs.

Names, mythology, uses and folk-lore

The plant has a variety of names listed by Grigson. These include such incomprehensible names as *ekkel-girse,* and *yirning girse.* In the North of England it was known as *earning girse* which I understand refers to its properties of curdling.

In the Scottish Highlands it was said to protect from witches (Grigson). He quotes an author from Colonsay (McNeil 1910) who wrote that two ladies were protecting one of their new born to make sure it would not be exchanged by the fairies. Two fairies did come: one said, let us take the child, but the other said no – for the baby was protected by the milk obtained from cows which had eaten the butterwort plant.

Butterwort produces a strong bactericide which prevents insects from rotting while they are being digested. According to Linnaeus, this property has long been known by northern Europeans, who applied butterwort leaves to the sores of cattle to promote healing. Additionally, butterwort leaves were used to curdle milk and form a buttermilk-like fermented milk product called filmjölk (in Sweden). (Wikipedia).

Allen and Hatfield refer to the plants providing material which could treat chapped hands and a syrup which would free blocked bowels - the same mixed with butter could assist in treating liver obstructions.

There were some folk-lore traditions which suggested that the plant could give rot to sheep.

Pechey said that the plant could treat parts affected by pain if it was applied to them and that it was a good vulnerary herb – it could also treat ruptures in children!

There are two other butterworts seen in the U.K. – the ***large-flowered*** and the ***pale***. Both are rare and not seen in the areas covered by this book.

EYEBRIGHT

Euphrasia officianalis: Scrophulariaceae family

The plant: This is a plant which grows in undisturbed grassy areas. There are about thirty or more variants – but to the country walker the differences are of little importance. It is found throughout the country but is best described as locally common. Some types grow up to about twenty five cm or so – but this plant was only a few centimetres tall. It was photographed in Upper Weardale near the Middlehope Burn above Westgate. The plant is semi-parasitic – it lives on the roots of other plants.

The flowers: These were no more than about 5mm long and looked like little white spots when walking by. However look at the beauty of them when examined close up. They appear on spikes which are also leafy. The flowers can be seen from early Spring to late September: this flower was photographed in early July.

The leaves: Essentially these are oval but with sharply defined teeth.

Names, mythology, uses and folk-lore

It has a variety of names including *fairy flax* and *peeweets*. Milton referred to the use of Eyebright in his poem, *Paradise Lost,* when the Archangel anointed Adam's eyes with Euphrasie and Rue, and three drops from the Well of Life, until he could see death and the future of mankind. Its best known use has been for conjunctivitis – but other diseases in which it has been used include rheumatism, gout and bruises. Wordsworth wrote about it but confused the plant with a speedwell!

Foxglove

FOXGLOVE

Digitalis purpurea: *Scrophulariaceae family*

The plant: Most typically seen in damp woodlands – but is distributed widely growing best in acidic soils and will be seen on virtually every country walk at some point. In its first year the leaves form a rosette and it is from this ground level that the long flower spikes grow in the second year. The plant is usually a biennial one – but just sometimes it can be a relatively short lived perennial. Grows to 1.5m in height. It is seen throughout the U.K. and is common throughout.

The flowers: Seen between June and August these grow on long spikes and there can be fifty or more on each stem. Each arises singly from the stem. They are usually pink with dark purplish spots being about four centimetres long and one centimetre or so in width. The entrance to each flower bloom is "guarded" by a series of fine hairs.

The leaves: are large – up to twenty five cm or so in length and oval shaped. They are covered in small hairs and the leaves appear rather wrinkled.

Names, mythology, uses and folk-lore

A very large number of names have been devised for the foxglove. These include: *bunny rabbit's (mouth), witch's thimble, ladies thimble, goose/cow/fox flops, virgin's fingers, wild mercury* and many, many more. The foxglove name is just that – the fox's glove. It has also been given fairy associations.

In centuries gone by children who had gone missing might be assumed to have been abducted by fairies. They could be brought back under the influence of fox-glove magic. Equally when a mother discovered in her child's cradle a child uglier than she thought should be there, she might wonder if the child had been swapped by the fairies, a "changeling" being left behind. Feeding the baby with fox-glove tea, made from foxglove leaves, would not affect a changeling, confirming it to be of fairy origin. (Isabel Haldane, in 1625, gave a child foxglove tea under these circumstances – the child died!!).

As early as 1785, cardiac properties of the leaves were recognised. When given to people with heart failure and dropsy (ankle swelling) they would be improved. The active ingredient is a glycoside – digitalis – and digoxin is the synthetic derivative which is widely used in treating cardiac failure. Before this a weight of dried leaves would be prescribed – the effect could not always be anticipated for the drug's concentration varied. The dried leaves are still prescribed in oriental medicine.

Culpeper recommended it in an ointment for cleansing wounds and treating the *King's evil – scrofula* (TB of the skin) and also in the treatment of a *"scabby head"*. James Telfer, a Northumbrian shepherd turned school master, wrote a ballad about fairy plants and how they could work for and against you (*Border Ballads, 1825*). The foxglove is mentioned in Druid literature – *her (a girl) breasts were more white than the breast of a white swan; her cheeks more red than the foxglove* (Cwlhuch and Olwen – from the Druid Network).

MIMULUS

MONKEY FLOWER

Mimulus guttatus: *Scrophulariaceae*

The plant: likes its feet in water – seen by streams and in damp areas. Came to Europe from the Aleutian Islands between Alaska and Russia where the climate is pretty awful: it is cold and foggy and there are over 250 days of rain each year. Has adapted well to U.K. conditions and after first being planted as a garden plant it was soon seen in the wild – by 1824. Now it can be seen on the sides of many streams – as here by the River Pont in Ponteland, Newcastle upon Tyne. Grows to about fifty cm – but sometimes more. Has become naturalised quite widely but usually on lowland sites.

The flowers: are up to about four cm across. The lower lip is three lobed and the upper lip two. Small red spots can be seen in the corolla of the flower. Seen June to September.

The leaves: These are oval in shape: the upper ones are unstalked.

BLOOD-DROP-EMLETS

Mimulus luteus: *Scrophulariaceae*

The plant: usually seen by the side of streams and rivers, or in damp earth. The plants photographed were in Upper Teesdale at a height of about four hundred m and I have seen other large clusters on Cheviot in Northumberland at a height of about five hundred m. They are virtually absent in the south of England. Grow to about fifty cm and otherwise are much like the monkey flower except for the very striking markings on the flowers. The plants were first imported from Chile as garden plants in 1826 and like their cousins, the monkey flower, soon escaped the confines of gardens. However both the monkey flower and the blood-drop-emlets are still used extensively in gardens, for their striking flower displays. Are less common than the monkey flower.

The flowers: like the monkey flower except for the very striking red markings shown on the plants photographed. Flower June to September.

The leaves: Largely oval with the upper ones being unstalked and "clasping" the stem.

Names, mythology, uses and folk-lore

The plants are edible – but are very salty and one would not usually use the plant as a source of food. They are pollinated by bees. The plant seems not to have attracted modern herbalists. Their relatively recent introduction to the U.K. came after some of the older herbalists had lived.

Field speedwell

SPEEDWELL

Veronica species: *Scrophulariaceae*

The plants: There are many species of speedwell which are likely to be seen on any country ramble – and even on many well groomed lawns. There are upwards of twenty or so different speedwells in the U.K. Some are quite regional – but all have in common the flower shape, if not always exactly the same colour. The plants are low lying and many are creeping, never being more than fifteen to twenty cm tall. To identify the separate species requires a good plant identifier in the pocket, as well as an awareness of the surroundings.

The flowers: these are usually blue – some completely blue, and some with white markings. The blue can be a deep colour or it can be quite pale. The flowers are usually small and rarely more than about eight mm across. The main exception is the germander speedwell which is up to twelve mm in diameter. Most are spring flowers coming in to flower as early as March in one or two instances – for example the wall speedwell.

The leaves: are variable – but most are hairy or downy.

Names, mythology, uses and folk-lore

In the world there are about five hundred species of speedwell – and, as can be imagined there are many colloquial names. Perhaps the most consistent names are *cat's eyes* and *bird's eye* and also *gipsyweed*. Wikipedia maintains a good list of these.

Some of the species are edible, and are said by some to taste like cress, although as a foodstuff, this seems to be more a function of the North American varieties. The plants are often food for butterfly and moth caterpillars.

The plants have been used as a herbal tea in Austria for diseases of the nervous system, cardiac and respiratory systems, and also metabolism. Modern herbals describe its use in digestive disorders (the heath variety of speedwell).

Some species can spread aggressively in lawns, even the well kept lawns, and other speedwells are planted and grown as ground cover.

It is seen in many places and Grigson suggests that it is a plant of the roadside which speeds you well as you pass by! He said that in Ireland the germander variety was sewn on to clothes to keep the wearer safe from accidents, and a stylised form of the flower was used as a mascot-badge for an RAF squadron.

There is a legend which says that picking the flower will in some areas cause the birds to peck out your own eye or in other places not your eye, but your mother's. Some names feature the word "devil" and in some legends picking a flower will cause a storm to come. Destroy a flower paves the way for someone to take out revenge on you. Grigson actually describes it as a "sinister little plant".

Some herbal uses have included its use in the management of "tired" eyes (whatever that means) and for this a liquid preparation is used. It is also said to have been used for the treatment of jaundice (Allen and Hatfield).

Searching the internet for evidence of its food uses leads to a very large number of speedwell restaurants being uncovered – and also to a locally well-known cavern in the Peak District – the Speedwell Cavern near Castleton.

COMMON TOADFLAX

Linaria vulgaris: *Scrophulariaceae*

The plant: Common in England and much of Wales – less frequently seen in Scotland. Grows in dry grassy areas for the most part: this plant was photographed on the Durham Coastal Path.

The flowers: about two centimetres long and arranged typically with a pale yellow two-lipped upper lobe, and three lobed lower lip. The centre is yellow. They have a long lower spur. The flowers are usually seen in spikes: the plant here is just commencing in flower.

The leaves: Many can be seen on this plant – they are green, and narrow, and grow from the whole length of the stems.

Names, mythology, uses and folk-lore

Many names are linked to "mouth" – *rabbit's mouth, wild gapmouth, puppy dog's mouth, pig's mouth,* and similar. *Bread and butter* is another, as is *snapdragon.* Grigson gives a large list of colloquial names as do various internet sites. It has a reputation as a laxative and as a diuretic. Baker describes the flower being used in a saucer of cream as a "deadly, irresistible flytrap". It is an invasive plant: gardeners who pull it out, but who are careless enough to leave even a tiny fragment of root will find another plant, or plants, growing there. Best to let it live in the wild, for it can "take over" a garden!

IVY-LEAVED TOADFLAX

Cymbalaria muralis: *Scruphulariaceae*

The plant: The plant is seen throughout England and Wales, but less commonly in Scotland. Typically grows on rocks and garden walls, and on the sides of paths. It is a plant from Southern Europe and was probably introduced in to Britain in the seventeenth century. Grigson says that William Coys, an amateur botanist/gardener, was responsible. From that small beginning it is now a most ubiquitous plant seemingly able to grow in areas where there must be pretty well no nutrition. It is claimed to be a perennial trailing plant and, once present, is difficult to eradicate. A note of caution is needed – the United States department of Agriculture lists it as an annual. The plant does spread quickly attaining a height, at most, of five centimetres.

The flowers: Usually up to about one centimetre in greatest diameter. They appear to be five-petalled – but in fact are two-lipped: the upper is two lobed, and the lower three lobed. They are purplish in colour with a yellow centre. The plant flowers from spring to late autumn, the flowers being on a long stalk. The flowers are said to be *phototropic*. The flower moves towards light until it is fertilised when it turns away from the light, and the seed-pod becomes recurved forcing the seed in to crevices where it germinates and grows.

The leaves: These are stalked, ivy shaped and usually have five lobes.

Names, mythology, uses and folk-lore

Many names are given to the plant – these include *creeping Jenny, fleas and lice, mother of thousands, Aaron's beard, nanny goats' mouths* and *rabbits' mouths* among many others. It is said to be especially plentiful in Oxford – hence *Oxford weed*, and its other main name is *Kenilworth plant*. I can find no herbal uses for the plant in English herbals.

YELLOW RATTLE

Rhinanthus minor – Scrophulariaceae family

The plant: This plant comes in all shapes and sizes - from a few centimetres to sixty or seventy. It is semi-parasitic, living especially on grass roots. As a result it is usually seen on grassland, but also in grassy woods. This flower was pictured in a field near the village of Snod's Edge, in Durham County – the field was full of the plants.

The flowers: usually about fifteen mm long – but can be smaller or larger. The corolla is yellow and the tooth like structures are usually coloured blue on the upper lip and are very short. It flowers all summer long from May onwards. The seed pods rattle as the seed matures and the plant is disturbed in wind or when walking.

The leaves: Their shape is basically ovoid with toothed edges as seen in the photograph.

Names, mythology, uses and folk-lore

Yellow rattle has many colloquial names – these include *Gowk's shilling* in Scotland to *Gowk's sixpence* and *hen pennies* in Northumberland ("Gowk" is a cuckoo). Other names relate to the seed pods – *rattle-traps, pepper box, rattle grass, cock's comb,* and *shackle caps*. There seem to be very few herbal uses ascribed to it: Culpeppr suggests that it can be used in those "troubled with cough or dimness of sight".

However, it does have one important function in modern times: its semi-parasitic characteristic causes the grasses that yellow rattle thrives on to be limited where it is present. In doing so there is the opportunity for an increasing variety of wild flowers to appear to create an old-fashioned flowering meadow. There is such a meadow in the care of the Northumberland Wildlife Trust in Riding Mill, Northumberland. However, grass yields are correspondingly poorer – so farmers are not keen to have it on their land.

WILD MIGNONETTE

Reseda lutea: *Resedaceae*

The plant: A somewhat shrubby biennial – sometimes perennial – plant which favours waste-land areas, and any disturbed soils – especially when chalky. Is an opportunist plant in this regard. Grows to about seventy cm and is very similar to ***weld*** (not shown here but is of the same family – but weld grows taller, the flower spikes are much more compact in density but also much longer than the mignonette. Also the petals of the flowers are only four in number).

The flowers: are largely yellow in colour with six petals. Seen over mid-summer. The seeds are disseminated directly from the seed-pod but also by ants and birds.

The leaves: are finely pinnate – and unlike weld which has thin leaves.

Names, mythology, uses and folk-lore

Other names which it is known by include *yellow mignonette, base rocket, Italian rocket.* Despite a careful search I can find no uses being recorded for this plant.

There is also a garden variety of melilot – this is scented – whereas the wild mignonette has no scent.

Durham coastal path view

COMMON MALLOW

Malva sylvestris: *Malvaceae*

The plant: Common Mallow is described as a plant common in the south of England but relatively scarce elsewhere. It is my experience that the common mallow plant is widespread in the north of England and the flowers photographed here were pictured on Holy Island. It is a perennial plant and can grow to some 1-1.5m in height.

The flowers: These are lilac in colour with five petals each with several purple veins. The flowers appear in mid-summer and can be seen until the early autumn.

The leaves: The leaves are usually five lobed in structure, although at the base of the plant they are often rounded.

Names, mythology, uses and folk-lore

The common mallow is generally seen on land that has been disturbed and, in my experience, it is commonly seen on the sides of paths near the coast. The example photographed here was on Holy Island.

Common mallow has had medicinal uses described for many centuries. Whether it is malva sylvestris which is always being referred to is somewhat uncertain, but the whole mallow family seems to have common properties ascribed to them. Mallow is referred to in the Old Testament by Job – it says people about him were starving and writes "*they gnaw the dried and desolate ground, they pick mallow and the leaves of bushes, and to warm themselves the roots of broom.*" (Job: 30, 3-4). Job seems to be saying that the leaves are being eaten by desperate people who are starving: there are much more recent references to the leaves, particularly the young leaves, being a very good constituent of salads.

Descriptions of the common mallow often describe it as being "*full of mucilage*". Mucilage is what I would regard as an old fashioned term but referring to a mucous–like substance and the leaves, the stems, and the roots do contain a substantial amount of this mucous-like substance. It is soft and, as a consequence, the plants seem to have been used in poultices being applied to the body to treat swellings. The fruits of the mallow can be eaten and these have a somewhat cheesy-like taste and texture. The seeds have been used as a laxative in the past and in some parts of the country have been recommended for "*cleansing of the system*". The plants have also been used for treating coughs, sore throats, and a variety of chest problems. Culpeper describes the use of mallow roots as being cooling and digesting, resisting poison, and helping corrosions or gnawing of the bowels or any other part, as also ulcers in the bladder. Alan and Hatfield have collected a variety of uses for the mallow, including treatments for sore or strained eyes, for varicose veins, in treating toothache and teething pains, in those suffering kidney and urinary troubles, and a variety of other illnesses including gonorrhoea.

I have heard the plant referred to as a *cheese plant* simply reflecting the taste and texture of the seeds but Grigson gives a variety of other names as well including *rags and tatters, old man's bread* and *cheese and pancake plants.*

Gorse by the Durham coastal path

MUSK MALLOW

Malva moschata: *Malvaceae*

The plant: This is a perennial plant generally growing in dry but grassy places and the flowers here were photographed on a roadside embankment facing south. The plants grow to about sixty or seventy cm in height.

The flowers*:* Again there are five petals growing in clusters around the end of the flowering stems. They are pale pink and, in my opinion, very attractive.

The leaves*:* are three lobed in basic structure but the higher up the plant the leaf emerges the more lobed it appears. The plant is at its showiest in mid-summer and is best described as locally common rather than being common everywhere. The example pictured here was by a lay-by on the A69 road in July. A few days later these flowers suffered the fate of many roadside plants: an entire bed of them was strimmed away.

Names, mythology, uses and folk-lore

These appear not to be separately described in herbals: they are generally held to have similar properties to the other mallow plants.

OTHER MALLOWS: There are a number of mallows in the UK. The **dwarf mallow** tends to be found in the southern half of England. The flowers are similar to the *common mallow* but are much paler and the flower itself is only about one-third of the size. The **tree mallow** is an uncommon plant found mainly on coastal sites. This can grow to about 2.5m in height. Although uncommon in general, where there is a plant there may well be many in the area. It is a very striking plant and is always worth keeping an eye open for it. *Comfreys* are also sometimes referred to in discussions on mallow – this plant is considered elsewhere in this book.

COMMON SPOTTED ORCHID

Dactylorhiza fuchsii: *Orchidaceae*

EARLY PURPLE ORCHID

Orchis mascula: *Orchidaceae*

The plants: relatively common orchids seen mainly in open woodlands and meadows – and can grow to about forty cm for the early purple and a little higher for the common spotted. Early purple is seen in May, and the common spotted in June to August. A characteristic of the leaves is that they are spotted – see inset picture – and the flower stem grows from a basal rosette. Prefer calcareous or neutral soils – these plants were growing in the upper part of Slitt Wood in Weardale. There are some excellent places to see them in the north-east of England – the Durham coastal path, and the disused rail-tracks around Scots Gap had abundant numbers. They are also relatively easily found on Holy Island.

The flowers: the flowers are the typical orchid flower as perceived by many who search out wild flowers. The lower lip is large and is three-lobed. The early purple is characterised by a long spur. The early purple colour is a pink-purple and the common spotted somewhat lighter. They are about one cm across and a little longer than this.

The leaves: these are arranged in a basal rosette and appear well before the flowers and flower stalk but, as here, may be camouflaged by surrounding grass. They are green in colour and are characterised by the dark spots on them. They are lanceolate in shape. There can be stem leaves.

Caution: Orchids can be notoriously difficult to identify and often one plant can mimic another – or even cross-pollinate to produce a variety of hybrids. The early purple is a little less common than the common spotted orchid. The leaves in both are arranged as a basal rosette of green leaves bearing dark spots. Leaves also emerge from the stem well away from the basal rosette – where they tend to be narrower. The flower colours are much as shown in the photographs, and sometimes the common spotted is confused with the Heath Spotted-orchid. The early purple has a long spur on the flower. The early purple also tends to be smaller. The heath spotted favours damp acidic soils – for example, moorland whereas the common and early spotted orchids favour calcareous soils.

Names, mythology, uses and folk-lore

This, or the early purple, have been called the Gethsemane, or Cross, flower – it is said that they grew at the base of the cross on which Christ was crucified and the blood which dropped from his body landed on the plant and marked the leaves. Shakespeare referred to the early purple in Hamlet, in Act 4, Scene 7: *"There with fantastic garland did she* (Ophelia) *come, of crow flowers, nettles, daises and long purples, that liberal shepherds give a grosser name....."*

Orchids have two tubers and these have acquired male anatomical associations. In an operation to remove or reposition a testis the terms orchidectomy (removal) or orchidopexy (repositioning) are used by the surgeon. This morphologic association has given the plants aphrodisiac properties in mythology. The tubers are the parts with these described properties. The tubers themselves will in the one be firm – this one is developing and will be the plant food source for the coming year's growth and is the one said to have the aphrodisiac properties. The other is softer, or slacker, - this one is the tuber feeding this year's plant. Dioscorides in his de Materia Medica written in the first century A.D. described the use of the slacker tubers to be given to women (Thessalonian women) to reduce desire presumably while their men-folk were away (Grigson). The aphrodisiac properties in orchid mythology are just that – confined to mythology. Digging up the orchids to examine the tubers may be against the law – so do not do so.

CHALK FRAGRANT ORCHID

Gymnadenia conopsea: *Orchidaceae*

The plant: this orchid grows on calcareous soils and on dry grassland. They can be locally very common when the smell from them can be especially obvious – a bit like carnations. Most common in southern England – but this plant was seen on a bank-side in upper Teesdale. In favourable areas can grow to sixty cm – but usually much less: the plant here, was no more than about sixteen cm tall. There are a number of sub-species: this plant is probably the *borealis* variety which is seen in north-eastern England and in Scotland.

The flowers: Usually pink but as ever with orchids can vary – in this case from almost white to dark purple. Flowers in June-August. The flower spikes may just have a few flowers – but can have as many as two hundred or more. They exhibit a long spur, and the lip is lobular in three lobes.

The leaves: Tend to be fairly short and lanceolate, concentrated towards the base of the plant, but thinner leaves grow directly from the stem.

I can find no listing of other names, no mythology and herbal uses attributed to this flower. This orchid can usually be distinguished from other orchids by its distinctive flowers, the sites of its growth, and the strong fragrance which can arise. The legends which relate to the tubers relate to all the orchidaceae (see early purple orchid).

Upper Weardale view

NORTHERN MARSH ORCHID

Dactylorhiza purpurella: *Orchidaceae*

The plant: Seen mainly in northern parts of Britain although not very common in Scotland. Overall it is scarce and where-ever it grows is not seen in large concentrations. This plant was found in a ditch in Upper Weardale at the edge of a meadow, and a number can be seen in the damp areas of Holy island, Northumberland. Generally grows in damp grassland. It is a small plant – I have never seen one more than about fifteen to twenty cm. tall but descriptions suggest that it can be up to sixty cm. in height.

The flowers: Appear in July usually. The flower is reddish-purple and the lower lip is lobulated – but you have to look hard to see the outline of the lobes.

The leaves: They are generally narrow and plain green. The leaves grow at the base of the plant and also appear in much the same size along the plant's flower stem.

Names, mythology, uses and folk-lore

There is no folk-lore that I have been able to find. The species was first recognised as a distinct form of Dwarf Purple Orchid in 1920 by a family called Stephenson (David Lang – see bibliography). A characteristic of the plant is the flower stem which has the appearance of having been cut off at its end. Can be confused with the Broad-leaved Marsh Orchid, but this plant flowers much earlier. It can hybridise with many other orchids: Lang describes hybrids with Frog Orchid, Fragrant Orchid, Common Spotted-orchid, Heath Spotted-orchid, Southern Marsh-orchid, Early Marsh-orchid and Broad-leaved Marsh-orchid. So beware – it is not always easy to identify!

PYRAMIDAL ORCHID

Anacamptis pyramidalis: *Orchidaceae*

The plant: Grows on calcareous grounds and on sand-dunes. This pair was photographed on Holy Island in July. Fairly common in southern England – especially on the chalk downs – but can be seen in many parts of the country especially the west. Less common on the east coast.

The flowers: appear in spikes at the end of stems of usually twenty cm in length, but can grow taller. When they first appear the flowers appear at the base of the flowering area of the spike and the structure appears pyramidal, as here: when all are in flower they appear to be more like tightly clustered spheres. The flowers are pink to red and the lower lip is divided in to three well-defined lobes. The flowers appear in high summer from June to August.

The leaves: The basal leaves, usually three to five in number are evident in the winter and spring time – but when the flower spikes appear they can appear quite shrivelled. Around six leaves arise from the stems as the flowering develops. All are quite thin and green and are linear in shape with a terminal point.

There seem to be no regularly described uses attributed specifically to this orchid, although the more general comments relating to orchids (see *common spotted orchid*) apply.

Marsh Marigold field in Teesdale

MARSH HELLEBORINE

Epipactus palustris: *Orchidaceae*

This plant grows, as the name suggests, in marshy land including dune slacks: this plant was on Holy Island and was photographed in the summer months. The flower spikes are open and usually contain up to twenty flowers. There are usually many lanceolate shaped leaves. The plants are seen most commonly in the south and the west of England and Wales. Not often seen in the south of Scotland and rare elsewhere. It is thought that the number of colonies is declining as wetlands become increasingly drained.

The flowers: seen close up the flowers seem most orchid like of all the helleborines and they have been compared with the common garden centre orchids of the Cymbidium family. Flowers appear from July into August. The lower lip is white and frilly at its edges. The upper white petals are sometimes marked with pink. The sepals are often a brownish or reddish green.

The leaves: These are broad towards the base and narrower further along the stem.

As with the other orchids there is a singular lack of associated mythology and folk-lore.

TOOTHWORT

Lathraea squamaria: *Orobanchaceae*

The plant: a very strange looking plant of woodland floors. It is parasitic and perennial. Lives on the roots of woody shrubs mainly. Contains no chlorophyll. The part of the plant below the ground contains leaves, or leaf like structures and above ground the only part which appears for a short season is the flowering stem. Here the flowers are yet to open – but when I went back a few days later the plant had disappeared. The plant was seen in Slitt Wood near Westgate in Weardale. Although seen in many parts of the country it is relatively uncommon. It grows to about twenty cm or so.

The flowers: I have never seen the flowers but they are said to be tubular in structure, about eighteen mm long and either a pale lilac or creamy white in colour. Flowers are present for a short period in April to May only.

Leaves: see above. There are no true leaves.

Names, mythology, uses and folk-lore

Culpeper says that the plant is good for easing pains in the side and bowels – and, when boiled, is good for the treatment of green wounds and ulcers. Pechey is more precise in its uses for which he, presumably, used it. Two drams of the powder taken in broth on each of forty consecutive days, treats ruptures, inward wounds and diseases from defluxions.

Note: both Culpeper and Pechey describe the toothwort as a member of the Dentaria family whereas more modern herbalists describe it as a plant of the Lathraea group. Both families of plants exist today so one hopes that, despite the confusion over genus, it is the same plant which is being discussed.

Grigson says that the flowering stem becomes purple in colour at its tip and as it climbs past the flowers becomes pale pink. In woods it is usually seen before the bluebell. Grigson states that one colloquial name is *corpse flower* – allegedly it has grown from a corpse.

COMMON DOG-VIOLET

Viola riviniana: *Violaceaceae*

The plant: is a plant of early spring and seen in hedge backs, woodland, river banks, and especially on chalky soil. Where-ever a violet is seen a primrose will not be far away. (Here a barren strawberry intrudes in to the picture). The photograph was taken in Slitt Wood in Weardale above Westgate and by the Middlehope Burn. The plant is low lying, never getting above about ten cm in height.

The flowers: are varying shades of blue or blue-purple and they exhibit a pale spur which can be seen in the photograph in the two lower violets, the spur heading behind the plant. The flowers are usually about fifteen mm across but sometimes larger ones are seen up to about twenty five mm. The flowers are seen from March to May.

The leaves: are roughly shaped like a heart outline and are on stalks. Usually hairy.

Names, mythology, uses and folk-lore

Names: the descriptor "dog" often signifies a plant that is regarded to be "lesser" than others of the same species. The shape of the spur is a little like a cuckoo's heel - and the name of *cuckoo's shoe* or *stocking* is sometimes used in Shropshire and also the north of Scotland. An old name in Cheshire is *shoes and stockings*.

Modern herbals by and large ignore the dog violets, although Culpeper describes a long list of uses for violets in general. Treating cholera, cooling fevers, and quinsy is effected with the leaves, and the leaves have also been recommended for treating "falling sickness" in children (presumably this means epilepsy). Fresh leaves and dried flowers are described by Culpeper as being good for pleurisy and also for jaundice. The flowers are said, also by Culpeper, to make an excellent cordial when mixed with lemon juice or oil of vitriol. I am somewhat uncertain of its substance. Probably it refers to an acid solution. Vitriol is a synonym for sulphuric acid!!

Simply enjoy the plant for its beauty – and its heralding of Spring!

There are a number of violets – and the **heath dog violet** is also shown. Almost the same as the common violet it can be distinguished by its height for it does grow taller, and the spur which is short and more a green or greenish-yellow colour. In addition there are no basal leaves – the basal leaves may not be easy to see in any violet given the usually dense nature of the grass and other plants surrounding it. Others you might see are the **early dog violet**, which is small and has pale violet flowers; the **marsh violet** which is found only in marshy areas and the **sweet violet** which has white flowers, but occasionally violet instead.

WILD PANSY/HEARTSEASE

Viola arvensis, tricolor, and lutea: *Violaceae*

The plants: there are several species of wild pansy to be found. There is also a wide variety of colours – and mostly very striking. Perhaps the most striking of all is coming across considerable numbers of the plants high up in Weardale and Teesdale fells, including a rare yellow mountain pansy. They are small plants and some are creepers, never growing taller than about ten to twelve cm depending on the site. The *heartsease* and the *field pansy* are annuals – although a yellow sub-species of heartsease (*v. tricolor. ssp curtisii*) is a perennial.

The flowers: are open from April/May to mid-August. Usually between fifteen and thirty mm in diameter.

The leaves: in general these are mainly kidney shaped.

Names, mythology, uses and folk-lore

Grigson and Wikipedia give a number of names. Some of these relate to kissing and others include *heart's delight* and *three faces in a hood*. Grigson gives one colloquial name as *Trinity Violet*. Whether this relates to the usual time approximately of flowering, or to the three main colours present on many of the flowers, is uncertain although I think that the evidence suggests a link to the Holy Trinity. Culpeper suggests that it is the church festival of Trinity. *"This is that herb which such physicians are licensed to blaspheme by authority, without danger of having their tongues burned through with an hot iron, called an herb of the Trinity. It is also called by those who are more moderate, Three faces in a Hood, Live in Idleness, or Cull me to you, and in Sussex we call them Pancies."*

Shakespeare refers to the plant in Midsummer Night's Dream when he describes Oberon squeezing the juice of wild pansy to the sleeping Titania's eyes so that she would fall in love with Bottom when she wakened.

Gerard said that it was difficult to remove the mountain pansy from its upland site and plant in the garden.

Culpeper has several uses for the plant saying that the spirit from it is useful in treating convulsions in children and the falling sickness as well being good for inflammation of the lungs and breast, pleurisy, scabs, itch, &c. However he gives the plant another use – *"A strong decoction of the herbs and flowers (if you will you may make into syrup) is an excellent cure for the French pox, the herb being a gallant antivenerean: and the antivenereans are the best cure for that disease, far better and safer than to torment them with the flux, divers foreign physicians have confessed."*

Wordsworth wrote about the pansy in his poem *Intimations of Immortality*:

> But there's a tree, of many, one,
> A single field which I have look'd upon
> Both of them speak of something that is gone:
> The pansy at my feet
> Doth the same tale repeat............

The mountain pansy and the heartsease or wild pansy are thought by cross breeding to be the forerunner of the garden plant we know today.

Mountain pansy

COMMON STORK'S-BILL

Erodium cicutarium: *Geraniaceae*

The plant: can be found almost anywhere. In North America, where it is generally regarded as a weed, it is an annual towards the north and a biennial in the warmer south. In the U.K it is an annual. Generally found in dry, and often sandy, places. This plant was growing among the dunes at Seaton Sluice in Northumberland. Under favourable circumstances it can grow as high as thirty cm: this plant was much lower. It is a hairy plant, and a somewhat sticky plant to handle.

The flowers: about one cm in diameter with five purplish-pink petals. The petals are often seen strewn on the ground beside the plant – they seem to be very loosely attached. Sometimes are dark spotted towards their base. Flowers from about May to September. Commoner in the southern part of the country than in the north.

The leaves: these are, as the picture shows, finely divided.

Names, mythology, uses and folk-lore

Herbalists seem to have ignored this plant – and even colloquial names for it are few and far between.

DOVES FOOT CRANE'S-BILL

Geranium molle: *Geraniaceae*

The plant: a low-lying annual plant with spreading and branched stems. Looked at close up they appear hairy. Never more than twenty cm long, but do not grow upwards in height. Often seen on road-side verges as was this one near the A68 in Tynedale and in dry, often grassy, places.

The flowers: this is quite typical – about eight mm across, five symmetrically notched petals with purple anthers. Appear between April and mid-summer. They are mainly pink but with well demarcated vein-like markings.

The leaves: in overall outline are rounded but with deep indentations to form five – sometimes seven – lobes.

Names, mythology, uses and folk-lore

As ever there is a variety of names for this plant which is commoner in the south than the north of England. *Dove's foot* or *dove's foot geranium, cranesbill geranium, soft geranium,* are but a few. Grigson maintains that the name should be Dove's Foot and nothing else - other than one or two colloquial names such as *jam tarts.*

Touch the plant and you will note just how soft it is. It is a vulnerary plant – useful in wound healing and Gerard also describes its use in the treatment of ruptures (herniae). Gerard describes beating and drying all parts of the plant and dissolving the powder in claret and taking this internally daily for twenty one days, will cure all ruptures! The only exception is in the elderly when the powder of nine dried and dead red snails (without shells) should be added to the drink! If I get a hernia I will be content to have a routine modern operation!

HERB ROBERT

Geranium Robertianum – *Geraniaceae*

The plant: shade loving – seen in woodlands rocky places – even on walls as here. Can grow to thirty cm. Is an annual.

The flowers: just over a cm in diameter with five deep pink petals and profuse yellow-orange pollen.

The leaves: deeply cut in to up to five lobes often seeming to be separate leaves. Hairy.

Names, mythology, uses and folk-lore

Despite the descriptor "herb" comparatively few uses seem to be described – these include usefulness in people weakened by long term illness. Lady Wilkinson describes the use of juice from the root to cure all manner of ear complaints. She also describes mixing the seeds with pepper and myrrh to treat spinal cramps. Allen and Hatfield describe Irish uses for it – gall stones, kidney stones and stomach gripe, and red-water fever in cattle. They also describe its use in Britain for managing gout and to reduce blood sugar levels in diabetes mellitus.

The plant is smelly when brought in to the house. It also has magical attributions – for example, one of its colloquial names is *death-come-quickly* (Grigson). Robin Goodfellow, a mischievous elf, was also associated with the plant but who haunted houses and woodlands, and from whom wood-lice would drop!

In Germany it has been called Ruprechtskraut (Ruprecht's herb or cabbage) Ruprecht is an elf, dressed in red, who travels with Father Christmas and who wields a stick against naughty children encountered on the way. The herb may also have links with St Robert of Salzburg. However, a very good source of information on this plant can be found at **http://www.dalswildlifesite.com/herbrobert.htm**

BLOODY CRANE'S-BILL

Geranium sanguineum - Geraniaceae

The plant: The bloody crane's-bill is mainly a coastal plant – it is also the county flower for Northumberland. It is seen in limestone areas – for example it is present in great profusion in parts of the Yorkshire Dales. This one was growing in the sand-dunes at Seaton Sluice, South-east Northumberland. Grows to twenty five cm at most, and the plants generally present in clumps. Several varieties are seen at Seaton Sluice. It is a plant best regarded as locally common – although it is rarely seen in South-east England or the North-west of Scotland.

The flowers: Tend to be a purple, rather than red, colour – not a healthy blood colour. They are about 2.5cm in diameter and are seen singly on the stalks. A hairy plant! Like other crane's-bills the seed pods are elongated looking like a crane's-bill.

The leaves: These are deeply divided and this division extends almost to the base of the leaf – at first glance look like several leaves rather than one divided in to seven lobes approximately.

Names, mythology, uses and folk-lore

Grigson, the internet and other sources seem not to attribute other names to it. I can find no specific uses being ascribed to it – but, in common with crane's-bills it is a vulnerary plant – that is, it is useful for wound healing. Allen and Hatfield describe its use in children with diarrhoeae, and this appears to have been a specific use for it suggesting that this came about as a result of learned tradition rather than folk-lore.

MEADOW CRANE'S-BILL

Geranium pratense: *Geraniaceae*

The plant: A tall plant, growing up to seventy five cm. Seen in meadows and road-side verges. Prefers an alkaline soil. Easy to confuse with other crane's-bills – the flower colour and habitat are the best clues, although the colour is not always "definite". Common in North-east England – indeed common almost anywhere apart from the South-eastern corner of the country where it is seen less frequently and North-west Scotland where it is virtually absent.

The flowers: Five-petalled and sometimes the meadow crane's-bill florets appear almost diaphanous. Essentially the flower is blue, or lilac. Seen in summer – June to August. The seed pods are elongated, rather like a crane's-bill – hence the name of the plant.

The leaves: leaves are quite jagged and deeply divided into six or seven lobes.

The "domestic geranium" is unrelated to the crane's-bills – it is a Pelargonium.

Names, mythology, uses and folk-lore

There is an abundance of names given to the meadow crane's-bill. Among those trawled from the internet include *blue basins, Grace of God (*in Germany the name *Gottesgnade* has been used - Grigson), *gipsy* and *loving Andrews* – but the derivation of this last name has eluded me totally. It has few uses described.

The River Wear starts here

PERIWINKLE

Vinca major and Vinca minor: *Apocyanaceae*

The plants: two are presented here. They are the greater (V. major) and the lesser (V. minor) periwinkles. Different books give different descriptions to each of the plants from one another. I believe the best description is from Culpeper. He stated that the paler blue and white ones grew in woodlands and were the lesser variety, whilst the blue variety was the greater periwinkle but was only ever seen in gardens. That has now changed and both are seen in the wild. The greater periwinkle is an introduced plant but from many centuries ago, whilst the lesser one is either native or which may have been introduced earlier. Both are climbers and can either hug the ground or can grow up other plants and shrubs to a height of about one metre. They are plants which can become moderately invasive – but which are also used by gardeners as ground cover for unsightly areas. The plants are woody and evergreen.

The flowers: each flower has five petals. It is said that the flowers are up to five cm across but my experience of the wild plants is that they rarely exceed three cm across and not all are lesser periwinkles which tend to be a bit smaller. Both varieties flower in early spring.

The leaves: are shiny, dark green and in stalked pairs on both plants.

Names, mythology, uses and folk-lore

In Dorset they have been known as *St Candida's eyes* after a famous local healer of the mediaeval era. Other names include *cockle shells* and *old woman's eyes.*

The plants are native to Europe, parts of Africa and south-west Asia. One of the vinca species, V. rosea, produces the agent vincristine which is used in the treatment of some cancers, lymphomas and leukaemia.

Other uses have been described. If a man and a woman eat the leaves together this will cause love to occur between them (Culpeper). Another aphrodisiac use is quoted by Grigson who says that a fourteenth century prescription was for the powdered plants to be mixed with earthworm (presumably also powdered) and then put into food to be eaten would induce love-making. I suspect that the drug company Pfizer has no worries over competition for its drug Viagra from these preparations.

Pechey describes Vinca as a famous vulnerary herb. He advised its use in fluxes of the belly, for dysentery, for piles and for nose bleeds. He said it was also used for the overflowing of the courses (a use described also by the French) – and also for looseness and pains of the teeth. He also said that the leaves mixed with a frankincense cured a scrofulous tumour in a short time.

Allen and Hatfield said that the plants were used to treat cramps, and were also used in some parts as a sedative. They confirm the vulnerary value of the herb by describing the plants' widespread use in aiding the healing of cuts and bruises – and also for treating boils.

Durham Coastal path view

BIRD'S-FOOT TREFOIL

Lotus corniculatus: *Fabaceae*

The plant: grows to about ten to fifteen cm in grassy areas including road-side verges. It is a creeping perennial.

The flowers: are in heads about four or five cm in diameter, and sometimes larger. The individual flowers are small being about ten or twelve mm in length. The flower is typically that of a pea: there is a large upper petal or banner, the lower petal is usually two petals fused with a keel between them. The stamens are usually fused in to what is called a pistil. The calyx at the base of the flower is usually very small. Flowering season of this plant is from May to early autumn. They are yellow but in bud and as they are coming into bloom are often heavily pigmented in a red colour.

The leaves: the leaves appear trifoliate but are actually in groups of five with the lowest pair being basal.

Names, mythology, uses and folk-lore

The name of the plant comes from the appearance of the seed pods – see the photograph. The name is obvious!

There are numerous colloquial names. There are over seventy listed in Grigson and include: *lady's fingers, old woman's toe nails, lady's slipper, eggs and collop (bacon), craa taes, cheese-cake grass, yellow clover, Kitty two-shoes, Tommy tottles* and others including *Tom Thumb* and *Hop o' my thumb.*

Grigson describes the names as being neutral, evil or good. The associations with crows (crae's feet) implies evil and Tom Thumb is held to be a goblin—and, as such, the plant ought not to be picked. Tom Thumb has been variously associated with witch-craft and also as a somewhat endearing person, a dwarf of King Alfred and a supernaturally powerful being.

Culpeper gives the plants some major qualities and uses. Decoctions could be used as wound drinks and also to be applied to the wound. It is also capable of breaking up kidney stones and "driving them forth" if the decoction is drunk. It also treats ruptures when drunk (ruptures are hernias).

So it is a diminutive plant and yet one which has captured people's imagination with many uses being attributed to it. Modern herbals – at least the ones I have consulted – ignore the plant as far as I can tell.

GREATER BIRD'S-FOOT TREFOIL

Lotus pedunculatus: *Fabaceae*

The plant: this is one of the taller vetches growing, as it does, to about forty or fifty cm. This one was in a ditch – these plants favour damp places. It is downy and is a perennial.

The flowers: arise in loosely clustered florets forming a head at the end of a stalk. The flowers are yellow – unlike the lesser bird's foot trefoil which are reddish when young. The flowering season is from June to August.

The leaves: there are five leaflets to each stem: the basal pair are at the bottom of the leaf stalk, the remaining three appearing trifoliate.

The greater bird's foot trefoil seems generally to be considered under one heading of bird's foot trefoil, and without any separate names or traditions being associated with it. However, it is useful to see it here in order to distinguish one of these two plants from the other.

CLOVER

Trifolium pratense (red) and Trifolium repens (white) – *Fabaceae*

The plants: are quite similar: the red clover grows to about thirty to forty cm as does the white. The plants are superficially similar except for the colour of the flowers, the red is hairy and the white hairless and the white is a creeping plant. Both are perennial and both have trefoil leaves. If you see a white clover and it is not creeping then it is likely to be the **alsiker clover**.

The flowers: are so familiar to everyone. The flower heads are about two cm across, or a little larger, and consist of densely packed florets in the heads. They flower in the spring until about mid-autumn. The red clover pictured here has a six-spot Burnet moth feasting on it: these colourful moths are seen at the coast and very rarely, if at all, more than a mile or two from the coast. The plant was photographed on the Durham coastal path.

The leaves: are also well known. They are trifoliate, but occasionally more are seen. The leaves of both white and red have a whitish mark on them. The leaves are claimed to be the origin of the "shamrock" – but this attribution is also given to wood sorrel (q.v.).

Names, mythology, uses and folk-lore

The older herbalists usually called the plants trefoil and did not distinguish between the various types of clover except sometimes a yellow plant was also described (likely to have been the hop trefoil).

With such a well-known plant it was inevitable that many colloquial names will have arisen. Such names include *soukies* – from the children's' custom of pulling out a single floret and sucking the deep part to extract some of the "sweetness". *Broad grass, sleeping Maggie* and *Claver* are other common names. *Claver* is probably the name before clover and *Claver* has been incorporated in to place names. In some parts of the country a name given was *pinkies* which must run the risk of causing confusion to Scottish people for whom the little finger is the pinkie.

Four leaved clovers are said to bring luck but some clover plants have been shown to have many leaflets on the plant.

An infusion of clover is said to be a good cure for coughs. Other uses include being a foodstuff. The young leaves are sometimes incorporated into a salad and they may also be cooked like spinach and be incorporated in to spinach as a vegetable. The leaves can also be added to stir fries and soups. It is said that the flowers from each plant can be used as the starting point in wine making.

The trifoliate leaves had magical properties – hence the "luck" which it is said comes from finding a four-leaved plant. Bathing with red clover flowers is said to bring wealth and the flowers can also expel evil ghosts. White clover, if worn or placed around the house, is said to break evil spells.

The clover is closely related to *Melilot* from which the anticoagulant, dicoumarol, (Warfarin is the ubiquitous name for the product now used) was isolated.

Culpeper gives a large range of uses: against gout, for eye disease, preventing adder bites – and also good to treat them, in a poultice treats abscesses (imposthumes), and is a good wound healing plant.

Perhaps the most widespread use for clover now is as an animal fodder.

Apart from the *red* and *white clovers*, keep an eye open also for *alsike clover*, a white flower which gives way to pink as the flower ages, and the so-called **zig-zag clover** which looks like the usual red clover, but the stems are zig-zag in outline. Other clovers are less common although common sometimes where they are to be found – these include the **hare's foot clover**, a smaller plant and with white/off white flowers sometimes with a purple margin and the **knotted clover**.

COMMON RESTHARROW

Ononis repens: *Fabaceae*

The plants: tough-looking creeping perennial usually on calcareous soil.

The flowers: are a deep pink colour for the most part and appear from June to September.

The leaves: are hairy and feel sticky and almost succulent like. They are trifoliate.

Names, mythology, uses and folk-lore

Pechey recommends the plant – that is its root bark or the root itself for provoking urine, dispelling gravel and for easing the pain of the teeth. It – the root – also opens up obstructions of the liver being infused in wine, or boiled in posset drink and taken internally for some time.

Grigson reports that children in the north dug up the roots and chewed them – calling them Spanish, short for Spanish liquorice. If anyone feels like replicating this activity do not use too much for there are diuretic properties associated with the plant. He also reported that farmers disliked the plant for cows eating it would cause their milk to be tainted.

Other names include *wild liquorice, hen-gorse, stay-plough* and *stinking tam.*

HOP TREFOIL

Trifolium campestre: *Fabaceae*

The plant: A plant of grassland – it is an annual and can reach up to twenty cm or so especially if well supported.

The flowers: each floret is often only about four mm or so in length. They are tightly clustered into crowded flower heads which are about fifteen mm or a bit more in diameter. The flowers are yellow and can appear very much like black medick – but the flower heads change from yellow to brown and then appear like small hops. In flower for much of the summer until October.

The leaves: like the stems these are hairy and trifoliate – but the most distal leaflet is on a longer stalk.

Names, mythology, uses and folk-lore

The plant is included here to help differentiate this and the black medick from one another. Herbalists seem to ignore it and I can find no legends associated with it.

BLACK MEDICK (BUR CLOVER)

Medicago lupulina: *Fabaceae*

The plant: An annual and common plant seen in grassland, road-side verges and even waste ground areas. It never grows higher than about fifteen to twenty cm. The plant is downy.

The flowers: These are tiny and are tightly clustered together to form a flower head of eight or nine mm across. They are yellow in colour and can be seen all summer from May until late September or into October,

The leaves: are trifoliate.

Names, mythology, uses and folk-lore

A great many names for the *Black Medick* plant can be found in books and on the internet. *Nonesuch, dog clover, black hay* and *black nonesuch* are but some of the names which might be found. The plant is sometimes called **hop trefoil** – it is not, of course, that plant although outwardly the two can appear similar. They can be distinguished, however, by looking for evidence of hairs on the plants (favours evidence of black medick) and the head appears larger for the hop trefoil – up to fifteen mm across with the individual florets being about five mm long. The two are more readily distinguished from one or another when both are present together. The descriptor "black" refers to the colour of the seed pods when the plant is dying off.

Black medick can be cattle fodder. It is related to **Alfa-Alfa** which is a flowering plant in the pea family. This is very good for animal fodder and it has probably been used in pre-Roman and Greek civilisations for just this purpose as well as today.

In the roots are nitrogen fixing bacteria, as is the case with other legumes and fabaceae plants. It is also able to thrive on poor soil so can be a good crop where the land is of poor quality for the nitrogen will enhance the soil. *Black medick* is sometimes found in lawns. Usually the wish of the gardener is not to be a host to it – but the plant will improve soil quality.

It is closely related to *clover* and the *melilotus* (see *Ribbed Melilot*).

For such a common plant there is very little evidence that it has ever found a use in herbal medicine and there seems also to be a paucity of folk-lore relating to it – most unusual.

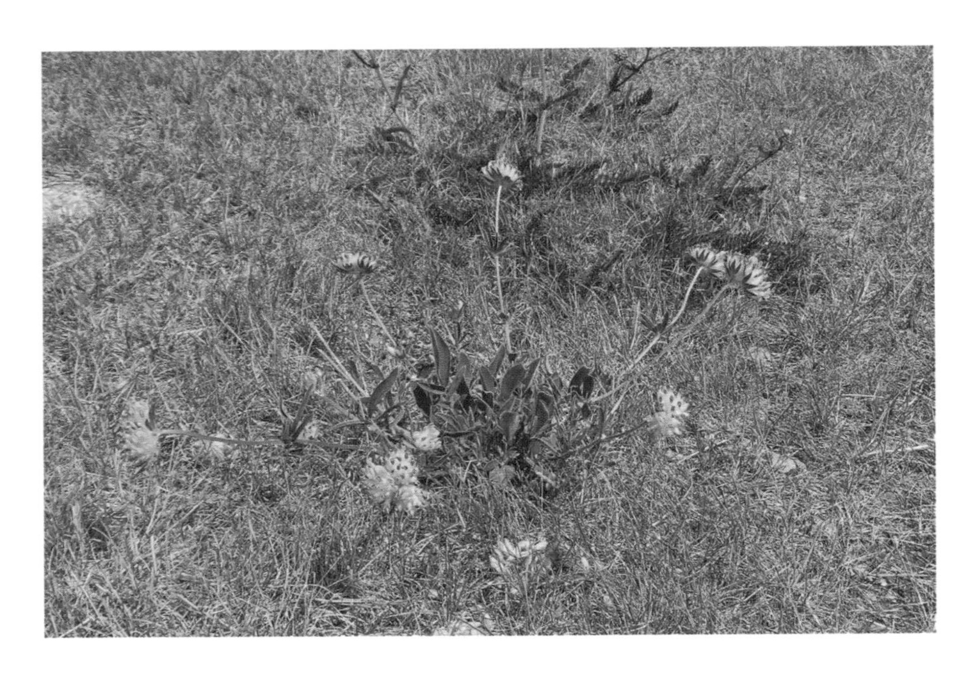

KIDNEY VETCH

Anthyllis vulneraria: *Fabaceae*

The plant: a perennial plant of dry grassland and exposed coastal areas. This one was photographed near the Durham coastal path on the cliffs. Hairy. Is seen throughout the U.K., Europe from the far north to the Mediterranean Sea, through Asia Minor, Iran, North Africa and Ethiopia. The small blue butterfly feeds on it. It is a hermaphrodite plant.

The flowers: usually yellow, but can be orange or even red. The flower heads are paired. The heads are about two or three cm across with multiple individual vetch-like florets. Long flowering season which is from May until the early autumn.

The leaves: the leaves are narrow.

Names, mythology, uses and folk-lore

It is sometimes listed as ***Lady's Finger*** rather than kidney vetch. Other names include *butter fingers, fingers and thumbs, yellow cow's foot, lambs' toes, pin cushion* and *wound wort Medicinal plant*.

As the name "vulneraria" suggests it is a plant associated with wound healing and Allen and Hatfield refer to this property but comment on the paucity of references to this – they could only identify two Gaelic references from the Scottish Highlands.

There are scattered medical references to the plant being used to treat coughs, as a laxative and in aiding wound healing – but it does seem to be largely ignored.

MEADOW VETCHLING

Lathyrus pratensis: *Fabaceae*

The plant: A perennial plant of grassland. Grows to about forty cm or so on Holy Island where this plant was photographed, but it is fairly common. Rather an obscure plant when seen in grassy meadows but the flowers are a bright yellow. It possesses no hairs.

The flowers: are about fifteen mm long and bright yellow – with some dark purplish streaks on the upper hood petal. In flower for much of the summer. The flowers are between four and eight approximately in number at the ends of the stalks.

The leaves: are narrow with large stipules arising at the base of the leaves. Tendrils arise from the angle area – usually just one.

Names, mythology, uses and folk-lore

Colloquial names seem to be shared with other fabaceae varieties – eg: *Lady's finger, fingers and thumbs* and *Tom Thumb*. It is sometimes named as a *vetch* and sometimes as *bird's foot trefoil (Lotus corniculata)*. There is really nothing written in those books I have consulted and on the various internet sites about the uses the plant has been put (apart from its use in animal fodder). If you know differently please let me know.

PURPLE MILK VETCH

Astralagus danicus: *Fabaceae*

The plant: a low lying vetch which is a creeping plant and is usually seen on dry grassland on calcareous soil. It is downy and those I have seen have been no more than about fifteen cm in height although it is said they grow to about thirty cm.

The flowers: about ten mm long and purple and are in fairly loose clusters at the ends of the stalks. Can be seen in early summer from May until July.

The leaves: the leaves are hairy and have up to a dozen pair of leaflets.

Names, mythology, uses and folk-lore

Very little is written in the usual places about this plant. It used to be a quite common constituent of cattle fodder and was claimed to improve milk yields, - hence its name. However, beyond that there is little published.

This flower was seen on Holy Island and the milk vetch plants in the area were rarely free of six-spot Burnet moths on them consuming the nectar.

The reason I include this plant here is that it is now an endangered species and possibly the best areas still for seeing it are in North-east England and South-east Scotland as well as some areas in East Anglia. It is virtually absent from the rest of the country. The possible reason for its decline is due to habitat destruction through agricultural development and lack of suitable grazing management. It is also thought that nitrogen from drifting crop spray, or atmospheric deposition, is affecting the plant. www.plantlife.org.uk/wild_plants/plant_species/purplemilkvetch.

RIBBED MELILOT

Melilotus officinalis: *Fabaceae*

The plant: difficult to distinguish from the golden melilot. On the ribbed the flowers have wings longer than the keels. Grows on rough, waste ground and is hairless. This plant was seen on the Durham Coastal path in July. It is a biennial. The plant was about seventy cm tall but can grow to almost twice that length. It is fairly common in the south of Britain but not seen so much in the north.

The flowers: are in long spikes and, quite simply, are yellow, but vetch-like in shape. Can be seen in mid-summer to about August.

The leaves: not easily seen here but are oblong and lightly toothed.

Names, mythology, uses and folk-lore

Other names include *common* or *yellow*. *King's Claver* is another name. Probably introduced to the U.K. in about the sixteenth century. Contains coumarin which gives a sweet odour to the plant.

The coumarin decays to dicoumarol if the plant becomes mouldy and a farmer in Wisconsin wondered why his cows were dying as a result of eating the melilot. They were dying of internal bleeding and this was eventually traced back to the melilot as the cause. It was, of course, the dicoumarol and this serendipitous observation led to the production of Warfarin, the anticoagulant for human use. It is still in widespread clinical use in humans today a century or so after the first observation was made.

The plant is also harvested as a source of the coumarin which is then converted in to rat poison – again the drug causes haemorrhage in the rat.

The nectar is good for bees – the plant is rich in nectar.

Ribbed melilot has also been used for the treatment of soils contaminated by dioxins. However, it seems to be singularly absent from the herbalists' books.

COMMON VETCH

Vicia sativa: *Fabaceae*

The plant: this vetch is a scrambling plant and can be seen pushing its way through grass or climbing up hedges: it can reach up to eighty cm or so.

The flowers: a typical pea flower with a large upper banner which is a pinkish-purple and a fused lower lip of similar colour with a central keel. The more proximal part of the banner especially can be quite pale. The flowers are about three cm in length and are arranged in pairs on the stem. The flowers are present for a good part of the summer from about May until September.

The leaves: There are up to about eight pairs of leaflets, though often fewer, which are downy and which end in a pair of tendrils.

Names, mythology, uses and folk-lore

The plant probably originates from the western part of Asia but has long been grown by farmers in this country, Europe, North America, southern Australia and so on – indeed many centuries of farming with the plant being sown for animal fodder.

Some of the names one sees seem quite obscure – these include *tare, wild tare, blue tan-fitch* and *fetches.* In the USA the plant is associated with Oregon – *Oregon vetch.*

The word tare is non-specific to the vetch family. Bible scholars may wonder if it is related to the Parable of the Tares (Matthew 13:24-30) – the answer is "no" for here the parable is probably relating to the plant **darnel**.

TUFTED VETCH

Vicia cracca: *Fabaceae*

The plant: this is a sprawling climbing plant which can reach considerable height if it has something to grow on such as a hedge. This plant was about two m. tall.

The flowers: the individual florets are about fifteen mm long and appear on pendulant spikes up to eight or nine cm in length. They are blue/purple and appear from early June until well in to August.

The leaves: are long consisting of up to ten or twelve pairs of narrow leaflets with a branched tendril, for climbing, at the end.

Names. mythology, uses and folk-lore

The plant seems to be accorded no herbal benefits – Culpeper, Gerard and Pechey ignore the plant, and Grigson says quite bluntly that it has no attributes.

Some other names are given to the plant including *wild vetch, huggaback* and *mouse's pease* all by Grigson.

BUGLOSS

Anchusa arvensis: *Boraginaceae*

The plant: This is a very deep rooted annual of arable land and any disturbed ground including road-side verges. It can reach fifty cm or so in height and is a coarsely hairy plant. Although it is an annual, personal experience suggests that even early eradication attempts in the garden usually fail – possibly because the seeds can survive in the ground for some years. It is not unattractive but it has great ability to spread quite rapidly.

The flowers: are small compared with the size of the plant being about six mm in diameter at the end of the stalks where they appear in small clusters. They are blue. In flower from May to October.

The leaves: are narrow with irregular edges and hairy. The lower ones are on stalks but the upper ones arise and clasp the stem.

Names, mythology, uses and folk-lore

Pechey describes the flowers as being of one leaf and that each flower produces four seeds. He said that it has great use in melancholy and hypochondriac diseases and the flowers are reckoned to be one of the four cordial flowers. Pechey went on to describe a person rescued from the falling sickness (probably epilepsy) by the constant use of the flowers in wine for six months. The recipe he gave for this was typical of Pechey – very complex and in looking at it through modern eyes it is difficult identifying the active ingredient(s), if any.

Pechey's recipe is: leaves of bugloss, borage, balm, fumitory, water cress and brook lime – each four handfuls; of July flowers, marigolds, borage flowers, and cowslips, each three handfuls; the outward bark of six oranges and of four lemons: all being cut and bruised, pour upon them four quarts of posset drink made with cider (roughly four or five litres); distil them in a cold still and mingle all the water. Take three ounces (ninety ml/gm) night and morning.

Gerard recommended its use (the roots boiled in wine) for driving forth the measles and smallpox if it is drunk in the early stages in hot beer. He also reported that the gentlewomen of France painted their faces with the roots. Gerard put all the alkanets together which includes borage.

Culpeper said that the plant had the same "virtues" as borage and that the roots of either are seldom used. He reported that borage cheered the heart and helped the drooping spirits, quoting Disocorides in this.

Modern uses include using the leaves in salad although usually the reference is to the closely related flower borage. Woodruff leaves and the bugloss leaf make the classical flavouring in the summer drink Pimms (Ian Burrows).

COMFREY

COMMON COMFREY

Symphytum officinale: *Boraginaceae – includes ROUGH COMFREY – S. Asperum*

RUSSIAN COMFREY

Simphytum x Uplandicum: *Boraginaceae*

HIDCOTE BLUE

S. Asperum x grandiflorum x officinale

I have decided to consider all four plants together – but with some trepidation. Comfrey happily cross-breeds and it is possible that I am classifying one plant or another incorrectly. For example, the plant I label Russian Comfrey may be a common comfrey, as indeed could the Hidcote Blue one be not a Hidcote blue but also a common comfrey.

The plants are best considered together – but recognising that all may be separate sub-species. Most turn out to be garden escapees and all the plants photographed here have been fairly close to habitation. The blue one was photographed on the Wannie Line disused-rail track in Northumberland within a few hundred yards of Scots Gap, and the others have been photographed either on Holy Island or in a field managed by the Northumberland Wild-life Trust in Riding Mill.

The plant: Tall perennial plants reaching to about one metre. Usually hairy.

The flowers: these are bell-shaped, sometimes more tubular, and generally from ten to eighteen mm. long. The flowering season is from May to August.

The leaves: overall these are oval in shape and are hairy. The plant dies down in the autumn but will re-appear the following spring.

Names, mythology, uses and folk-lore

The plants have been known in the U.K. for a number of centuries. Pechey describes it as an excellent wound herb. It is mucilaginous and "*qualifies the Acrimony of the Humours*". He describes its use in managing fluxes, and for tuberculosis. Pechey describes cutting up the herb and applying it to leather and thence to the affected part. Doing this it eases the pain of gout, cures "eating" (e,g: infiltrating) ulcers, and helps unite broken bones. Over a century later Culpeper describes very similar uses – but adds that it is effective in treating bleeding ulcers, and areas affected by gout and painful joints. It also treats moist ulcers, gangrene, mortification and the like – and this profile was based on his own observations.

Allen and Hatfield also describe the plant's use for digestive problems in horses and poultry, diarrhoea in cattle – and in swine fever.

FORGET-ME-NOT

Myositis arvensis – *Boraginaceae*

The plant: seen almost anywhere. Some prefer woodlands, some boggy areas and some bare areas and grassland. Various varieties may be creeping plants, others bush-like. Some are annuals and others perennials. I have seen over thirty listed.

The flowers: the flower is a lovely shade of blue with a yellow/white central area. Some varieties start with yellow flowers which turn to blue. All are hairy but in some varieties the hairs appear suppressed – they are tiny. Season lasts from April to September although individual varieties occupy only part of the season in flower. For the most part the flowers are only about two mm in diameter – but some varieties, for example, the wood forget-me-not can be up to seven or eight mm in diameter.

The leaves: the lowest, basal leaves, form a rosette usually, but leaves also arise from the stem. They are more-or-less oblong in shape.

Names, mythology, folk-lore and uses

There is a wonderful literature available describing the origin of the name – Wikipedia has a good article on the plant which seems well-referenced. The name may have been first translated to the English in the 15th Century or thereabouts. The French was *ne m'oubliez pas* (do not forget me). A German legend is that a Knight, in the Middle Ages, was about to go off with his army and was taking a last walk with his beloved, already in his armour. They were walking along a river path when he slipped and fell in. As he fell he grabbed a plant and threw it to his lady shouting *vergiss mein nicht* (do not forget me) for he knew that he was unable to swim in his armour.

However the story which appeals to me most is one that describes God naming all the plants but overlooking the little blue and yellow flowered plant. The plant shouted to God "*do not forget me*" and God responded by saying "*That shall be your name*".

Henry IVth used the plant as a symbol in his exile, and in modern times Newfoundland used the forget-me-not as a symbol of remembrance for World War 1 and 2 although it has increasingly used the poppy in its acts of remembrance.

Lady Wilkinson wrote that Pliny suggested that forget-me-not found in Egypt, if picked on the 27th of Thoth (roughly August time), and the juice used to anoint the eyes on first getting up, and before speaking, would ensure that the eyes will be free of weakness in the coming year.

I cannot find any herbal uses being ascribed to the plant – rather unusual given its ubiquitous nature. Just enjoy its beauty when you find one. (If a plant grows in the garden my experience is that you will soon have many).

Varieties to look out for include: ***wood forget-me-not, water forget-me-not, field forget-me-not, tufted forget-me-not.*** Less common varieties include: ***early, changing*** and ***creeping forget-me-nots.*** That still leaves well over twenty more to find here and abroad!

VIPER'S BUGLOSS

Echium vulgare: *Boraginaceae*

The plant: An upright plant of dry places especially on sandy soils – this plant was photographed on Holy Island. The plant grows to almost a metre in height.

The flowers: are funnel shaped and upwards of two cm in length. The flower is a bright blue and purple stamens can usually be seen protruding from the mouth of the flower. The flowers are multiple on terminal spikes as shown. They can usually be seen from June to August or September.

The leaves: are narrow and have a terminal point. The lower ones only are stalked – the remainder arise directly from the stem.

Names, mythology, uses and folk-lore

This is a most dramatic plant and is also quite hairy. It has many names including *blue weed, cat's tail, snake flower, wild bugloss, wild borage,* and *blue devil.* It is a plant seen through-out much of Europe and Northern Asia. The plant was introduced to North America and now, in parts, it is regarded as an invasive weed. The plant contains some fatty acids and is grown in some areas as an oil-seed crop.

The name "*Viper*" derives from the notion that the seed nut-lets resemble a Viper's head.

Culpeper says that the root is good for snake bites and for bites from venomous beasts. The roots, boiled in wine and drunk, increase milk in *nurses,* ie: lactating women.

Grigson wrote that any use of the plant could be traced back to the ancients such as Dioscorides.

BITTERSWEET
Solanium dulcamara: *Solanaceae*

The plant: A shrub-like perennial plant that grows to about one metre in height if the terrain is conducive to it. That terrain is likely to be one of scrub land, base of hedgerows where the soil is dry, and also on dunes – here the plant is growing on sand dunes at Seaton Sluice. It is quite woody towards its base which gives it the common name of *woody nightshade.*

The flower: appears in the summer from June to late August and are about twelve to fifteen mm in length. They appear in clusters which are pendulant: the flowers are purple. The fruits are red and egg shaped. The whole plant is poisonous but the red egg-shaped berries are especially so. Eventually these turn black.

The leaves: are oval in shape and pointed.

Names, mythology, uses and folk-lore

Names include *poisonous tea plant; felon plant* (although I can find no confirmation of this – the red berries were said to be used against felons), *robin under the hedge, witch flower* and *poison berry*.

Sixteenth century German physicians used the plant stalks against rheumatism, skin diseases and as a purgative. In more recent times the stems have been used against eczema. All red berries are assumed to have had magic powers: they were used in a wreath with holly around a horse's neck to protect it against being hag-ridden and there seems to have been a tradition in many places of using the berries to protect against witches. Culpeper refers to this usage and he recommended tying the berried stems around the neck of humans and animals.

The poisonous component is a Solanaceae alkaloid which I understand is like the alkaloids derived from Vinca. Solanine, a derivative of this alkaloid, can be extracted from the plant and used not only against fungal infections but also it will inhibit the growth of the gut organism Eschericia Coli, and the skin organism Staphylococcus Aureus which may cause skin infections.

Where-ever plants have been shown to have a drug effect giving a perceived high they have been used. Chewing the leaves can induce a narcotic effect and there are references to school-boys doing just this very many generations ago.

BUTTERBUR

Petasities Hybridus: *Asteraceae*

The plant: This grows in damp ground and especially flourishes on the banks of rivers and streams. The flowers appear before the leaves. The photographs show butterbur at the very early stage of development in Upper Weardale and the other picture shows the plant when the flowers are more or less dying off and the leaves are much bigger. It is a perennial.

***The flowers*:** The first sign of the flower bud appearing is a small mushroom-like plant emerging through the ground and this appearance has given rise to a number of its local names. The flower spikes are quite tough and they bear flowers which are a pinkish red in appearance. The plants themselves are single sex. Male plants tend to have larger flowers measuring up to about ten mm across whereas the female plants have smaller flowers up to about six mm across. They appear in March to May time and the flowers tend to die off as the leaves of the plant appear.

The leaves: These may be very large – up to one metre or so in diameter. They are roughly heart shaped and a "crowd" of butterbur plants can be identified in summer time by these very large leaves. The stalk of the plant makes the leaves and stalk look a little like rhubarb. These should not be confused with the plant Gunnera: this has long flower spikes. For the most part they have been planted but some "escape" and now appear as naturalised plants mainly in the southern half of the U.K.

Names, mythology, uses and folk-lore

As ever Grigson is a rich source of names for this plant and a few, taken from the list he presents, include *umbrella plant, umbrella leaves* and because of its appearance to rhubarb *gypsies' rhubarb, bog rhubarb,* and *snakes' rhubarb.* In the North East of England names such as *eldin, eldocken,* and *eldin docken* are given to the plant but I have been unable to determine how these names arose.

The name butterbur is widely known and comes from the habit that farmers, and especially farmers' wives, in the past would wrap butter destined for the market in leaves of butterbur.

The plant has been put to a number of uses. In recent times claims have been made that it is a valuable agent in treating allergies relating to grass, and the leaves have been studied in Austria relating to their traditional use as a tea or cold maceration in alcohol and as compresses for the treatment of infections, fever, flu, colds, hayfever and allergies. This was reported by Sylvia Fogel in 2013 as part of a broader paper looking at the *in-vitro* anti-inflammatory activities of seventy one Austrian traditional herbal drugs. In 2011 a paper was published in the Journal of Allergy and Clinical Immunology describing the use of an extract from the plant (ZE339) as being effective in treating or relieving the nasal obstruction which occurs secondary to allergic rhinitis.

The herbalist Culpeper described how the roots of the plants could be used in several settings, but most notably in those who wheeze or who are short-winded. This would fit, of course, with the modern plant extracts and research relating to them. Culpeper went on to describe its use as a diuretic and its value in killing tapeworms, which were common in those days. He also said that the root powder would dry up sores and take away all spots and blemishes of the skin and concluded with the following "*it were well if gentlewomen would keep this root preserved to help their neighbours. It is fit the rich should help the poor, for the poor cannot help themselves*"!! The name Petasities in its generic title is related to the Greek petasos which is a name for a wide brimmed hat to keep the sun off. Equally the butterbur leaf can be used to keep rain off just like an umbrella. An old German name for it is *pestwurz* (literally plague root) and this relates to attempts to treat victims of the plague in Germany with extracts of the root.

CAT'S-EAR

Hypochaeris radicata: *Asteraceae*

The plant: a perennial which can grow to fifty cm although is more usually somewhat shorter. Found in grassland particularly drier, rather than damper, areas.

The flowers: are yellow and arranged in a typical asteraceae fashion with outer ray florets and inner disc florets. The ray florets are much longer than the bracts from which they emerge. The stem is a little swollen below the heads. Each flower is about two cm in diameter although sometimes are a little larger. Flowers in mid-summer from June to August. The seeds are borne on feathery hairs.

The leaves: These are green and more or less oblong in a basal rosette. They have characteristic indented edges, giving a wavy appearance. These can just be made out towards the bottom of the picture.

Names, mythology, uses and folk-lore

it is always possible that old herbals can use different names for a plant – but I cannot find any references to this plant anywhere other than in Allen and Hatfield's book where the plants, if chewed, are said to staunch bleeding.

There are other cat's-ears to note. One is the **smooth cat's-ear** and the other is the **spotted cat's-ear**. Both are rare – or very rare – and are not seen in the north of England.

CHICORY

Cychorium intybus: *Asteraceae*

The plant: this plant was photographed in a quite typical setting – on the road-side in rural Northumberland. It is also to be seen in any grassy places where the soil is alkaline. It grows to about one metre and appears quite magisterial when in flower in the summer time. It is a perennial.

The flowers: grow on grooved and stiff stems and in heads as shown in the picture. Individual flowers are again typical of the asteraceae – with a group of central disc florets and outer ray florets all in this quite delicate sky-blue colour. The flowers are open in sunny weather, but usually only in the earlier part of the day. The flowers are blue – sometimes pale blue.

The leaves: The lower ones are stalked, the upper ones largely unstalked.

Names, mythology, uses and folk-lore

Grigson describes it as a plant "probably, but not certainly, native". Neither Gerard nor Lady Wilkinson mention it – even when searched for in its mediaeval name of *succory*. *Succory* was another name for it but again Gerard does not mention it in the edition which I have.

Culpeper, however, does not disappoint and he gives the plant a legion of uses: these include uses when the roots or leaves are boiled in wine and taken as a draught on an empty stomach. Under these conditions it drives out phlegmatic and choleric humours, opens obstructions of the liver, gall and spleen, helps the yellow jaundice and heat of the reins and urine, as well as treating dropsy and those of an "evil disposition" in their bodies – by reason of ill health or an evil diet (cachexia). Not satisfied with that lot he goes on to describe its use for the agues, for swoonings and passions of the heart, head-aches in children, swellings, inflammations etc., etc., - and it is very effectual for sore eyes.

The young leaves are sometimes used in salads, but they are rather bitter. The roots, dried and powdered, have been used as a substitute for coffee. There may be many who will remember the Camp coffee commonly used in the mid-twentieth century as a coffee substitute.

The plant was a "bitter-herb" referred to in the Bible in Exodus 6:v8 when the first Passover was instituted – this was the last night of the Israelites in Egypt – and they were to take an unblemished one-year old lamb, one per household, and on the fourteenth of the month they were to kill it and mark their door posts with some of the blood (to show they were Israelites and not Egyptians and that their first born would not be killed that night, but only the first born of the Egyptian households), and they were to eat the lamb roasted over the fire with unleavened bread and bitter herbs.

Note: Camp coffee was first made by a Scottish company in the later part of the 19th century. It is still available to purchase – for example, as I write this "Camp Chicory and Coffee" was available at Tesco's and no doubt from other stores as well. It contains Chicory 26% and coffee 4%.

Weardale flower pasture

COLT'S-FOOT

Tussilago farfara: *Asteraceae*

The plant: One of the earliest plants of spring time, the flowers appear first before the leaves. Commonly it is seen on land that has been disturbed and is especially seen at roadsides. Usually the land where it grows is relatively bare. Generally the flowering stem is ten to fifteen cm in height, although one has seen examples growing higher where the conditions are especially favourable. It is a creeping plant and is a perennial.

The flowers: These appear one at the end of each stem. The flowering stem is covered in a fine, downy fluff and it can be seen from the pictures that there is a series of overlying bracts. In common with other plants of this group, the flowers have a central disc of florets and an outer ray of more florets. Each floret is an individual flower. From these densely packed together florets seeds will arise as a "clock" similar to the dandelion.

The leaves: These do not appear until the flowers die off but when the leaves do appear they are almost heart-shaped in outline and can be up to about 20cm across.

Names, mythology, uses and folk-lore

It is the shape of the leaf which probably has resulted in the plant's name, i.e. the leaf is said to be the shape of the outline of a colt's foot. *Foal's foot* is another name of similar attribution. If one uses a little imagination the flowers can be seen to be rather suggestive of the brushes used by chimneysweeps in the past and in Yorkshire the plants have been known as *Sweeps' brushes*. There are innumerable many other names which Grigson lists and which can be found on the internet. In Northumberland they have been known as *Tussilagies*. *Clatterclogs* is a Cumbrian name.

Bacci Plant is a widespread name and relates to one or other of the uses that the plant has been put to. The name *Tussilago* gives a clue. Tussi relates to cough. The leaf has been dried and smoked as a herbal cure for dry coughs, but for children the leaves were boiled in water and then used – not smoked. Soaking the leaves in water and drinking the water has been used for asthma. Infusions of the leaves have been used to treat coughs. The leaves and flowers can be eaten in salads but it is not generally used for this purpose. The leaves, however, are especially rich in vitamin C. The flowers and stalks have been added to give flavouring to meat stews and the flowers are said to make a very fine country wine. Other uses include the quite ubiquitous use of the plant *"for purifying the blood"*, and in parts of Scotland an ointment from the roots has been used for sprains and joint swellings.

Culpeper gives it a series of other functions. In many of his descriptions of the uses of plants he implies that the sign under which the plant is associated will be pivotal to some of the plants' attributes. Culpeper says this is a plant under Venus and water distilled from boiling the plants, when drunk, is therefore good for treating the "hot agues". This is especially so when it is mixed with elderflower and nightshade. The distillate from boiling the leaves in water applied to a cloth and applied then to the head or stomach, has the same effect on the "hot agues" and, when used as a poultice, draws out inflammation. It has also been used in one form or another to treat St Anthony's Fire which can appear in the skin as redness arising from erysipelas or shingles - and also from ergot poisoning. This last used to happen in Germany and France where the climate is conducive to the growth on rye of a particular fungus rich in ergot. Gangrene, convulsions and hallucinations occur in the worst affected individuals eating food prepared with this rye-grain.

The use of the plant in chest complaints of upper respiratory tract infections is uncontroversial. Until the early years after the Second World War the plant was still described in the British Pharmaceutical Codex for treating upper respiratory tract problems.

It is a humble weed detested by gardeners but it has had many uses and I think it deserves a much higher status.

COMMON RAGWORT

Jacobaea vulgaris: Asteraceae
(old name was senecio jacobaea)

The plant: A very common grassland plant hated by horse owners especially. Best regarded as a biennial. Can grow to a metre in height. In general animals avoid foods toxic to them when food is in good supply but not otherwise: horse owners seem unwilling to have horses and ragwort in the same field. The problem really arises if ragwort is incorporated in to hay for it is likely then to be unrecognisable by the animal.

The flowers: arise at the ends of the stems and are in typical asteraceae form with an outer circumference of yellow ray florets and an inner cluster of almost orange disc florets. They appear between May and the autumn and are about fifteen mm in diameter. The seeds of the disc florets are downy but the ray floret seeds are hairless.

The leaves: are long and pinnate and are each deeply divided.

Names, mythology, uses and folk-lore

The plant has a wide range of names and these are listed in profusion both on the internet and by Grigson. One such name is *St James' Wort,* which implies a healing plant, and in this regard Culpeper gives several uses which include treating mouth ulcers, quinsy (abscesses around the tonsil), and the King's evil. The juice could heal green wounds – it cleanses and heals all old and filthy ulcers in the "privities". It can also help treat aches and pains, including sciatica. The attribution to St James may have arisen as the plant is flowering most profusely at about the time of St James' Day (July 25th).

The poison garden website is a good read on ragwort and is well worth reading in full if you have internet access (http://www.thepoisongarden.co.uk/atoz/jacobaea_vulgaris.htm). There are many descriptions of the name being a reference to the Jacobaeans but the web-site points out that this is wrong. Gerard described the plant as senecio jacobaea which must take it to about one hundred and fifty years before the battle of Culloden. The website also gives a Scottish name to the plant of *stinking Willie* for it grew in the path of the Duke of Cumberland – *Willie* – in the Jacobean war.

Burns wrote "Address to the deil" (deil is devil) and one verse refers to the ragwort:

Let warlocks grim, and wither'd hags
Tell how wi' you, on ragweed nags
They skim the muirs an' dizzy crags
Wi wicked speed
And in kirkyards renew their leagues
Owre howket dead.

Howket may come from howk which means digging – so may refer to graves.

Note: Ragwort is sometimes said by some to be a plant which must, by law, be controlled by the authorities and that a failure to report it is an offence. This is an exaggeration! A code of practice was issued after the Weeds Act was passed in Parliament in 2004. The code requires safe handling of weeds such as ragwort and that includes the duties of land-owners, live-stock owners and hay producers. The removal of ragwort, therefore, is often desirable, for it is an invasive weed, but any statutory requirement is covered by the Code of Practice issued in July 2004. The risk to cattle and horses is much greater from the dried plant in hay than from grazing in fields where it grows – livestock tends to avoid the plant under such circumstances.

CORNFLOWER
Centaurea cyanus: *Asteraceae*

The plant: The plant grows to about eighty cm and even more in the most clement areas. It is a creeper. Its favoured areas are arable land or where the ground has been disturbed. Thus it was seen commonly in areas such as cornfields which are ploughed and sown every year. It has become rare in recent years and is now generally held to be almost endangered – it is rarely seen "in the wild", and its sites are scarce. This flower was photographed in the walled garden on Holy Island. The reason for the decline seems to be attributed largely to the use of herbicides on corn fields and similar, which are given to eliminate any so-called "invading" plants that might result in impurities being present amongst the corn seeds.

The flowers: Typical of the aster family the flower heads are composites of an outer layer of florets aligned circumferentially and usually blue in colour. The inner florets are usually a deeper blue – almost a deep purple in colour. The photograph of the cornflower shows this arrangement well.

The leaves: These are not shown here – but the flowers are so characteristic that confusion should be most unlikely. The leaves are narrow and arise singly from the flower stem. The lower ones are sometimes lobed.

Names, mythology, uses and folk-lore

Internet sites, Grigson and others are all useful in trying to identify the commoner of the colloquial names that have been applied to the cornflower. Such names include *bluebottle* in Berwickshire, *bachelors' buttons, blue blaw, blue buttons, blue poppies brushes, corn blinks, corn bottle, millers' delight, cuckoo-pop hood, witch's thimbles* and *witch's bells*. A Swiss lady told me that in her German-speaking part of Switzerland the cornflower flowers are known as *Soldaten Knöpfchen – soldiers' buttons.*

In the older herbals it is described as having a whole range of uses. These include remedies against such disparate diseases as the plague, all manners of inflammations, fevers, poisonings and it is also said to be valuable for healing wounds.

Culpeper lists it under **"blue bottle"** and gives *corn flower* (sic) as an alternative name. One name mentioned by Culpeper is *hurt-sickle* which he presumes comes from its effect on the sickles which the plant turns (blunts) when cutting corn. Culpeper described the various prescriptions used for the giving of the plant: leaves and seeds boiled in wine are good for the plague; dried leaves given in plantain, horsetail or comfrey water, is effective for internal bleeding and also skin bruises – and in this preparation can treat scorpion stings. Cornflower juice put in to wounds, Culpeper says, will solder up the lips of the wound. An east-Anglian recipe was to bruise the flower and then put it in water and boil: the distillate was used in the eyes of elderly people to make them clearer and thus avoid the need for spectacles – known locally as *"break spectacles water"*.

Ann Finch, the Countess of Winchelsea, used to write in code (thus excluding the servants from seeing/understanding the letter) to her husband in the early 18th century to tempt him away from his work in the study for an assignation using the tale of Daphnis and Chloe:

Reading the softest Poetry, refuse, to view the subjects of each rural muse;
Nor let the busy compasses go round, when faery Cercles better mark the ground.
Rich Colours on the Vellum cease to lay, when ev'ry lawne much nobler can display,
When on the daz'ling poppy may be seen a glowing red, exceeding your carmine;
And for the blew (blue) *that o'er the Sea is borne, a brighter rises in our standing corn.*
Come then, my Dafnis,and the fields survey, and throo the groves, with your Ardelia stray.

DAISY

Bellis perennis: *Asteraceae*

The plant: It is very common throughout the U.K. This perennial plant grows well in short grass – and especially on regularly mowed lawns where some gardeners regard it as a weed – a plant in the wrong place. It is covered in a fine down. Usually very short but can grow if undisturbed to about ten centimetres.

The flowers: The flower head consists of an outer circumference of white, often pink tinged, floret petals, which are sterile: the yellow centre is also a mass of tiny florets – which each have a stamen and ovary – the fertile part of the plant. Usually the flower heads, which are singly placed on the stem, do not get much beyond fifteen mm. in diameter. The flower closes at night opening in bright light and sun-light and follows the sun – hence its name the Day's Eye or daisy. Seen between early spring and late autumn.

The leaves: Tend to be spoon shaped, broadening out from the base, and at the base of the plant: the flower stems emerge from this rosette of leaves.

Names, mythology uses and folk-lore

Gowan appears in many descriptive names. Gowan is a Northern name for any flower like a daisy. *Ewe gowan* comes from Northumberland (the daisy seems to grow well when sheep graze the herbage)*; May gowan* was used in the Berwick area. *Cats' posy* is a German based name, *bairnwort* and *bane-wort* are fairly common names and, for reasons which I do not know, it is associated with the twelve disciples.

It is known as a vulnerary herb – one that will aid wound healing. It has been used to treat sprains, eczema, bruises and infections in the skin. Precise numbers of the flowers were required for treating boils (seven) and two for toothache. The flowers needed to be picked from an area covered by one foot. Henry VIII ate platefuls of daisies for his stomach pains. Allen and Hatfield say that this property implies magic properties! Children – and some adults – make daisy chains with the flowering stems and wear them as necklets. Many authors have written about them – including Chaucer (prologue to The Legend of Good Women), Gerard Manley Hopkins, Lord Tennyson and Wordsworth – among many others. Young leaves and flower petals are sometimes used in salads.

DANDELION

Taraxacum officionale: *Asteraceae*

The plant: The dandelion is a very common plant – it is seen in many countries. Although very common in all parts of Europe until high altitude is reached, it is also a plant of the Middle East, Africa, Asia, the Americas and Australasia. In the U.K. it is usually seen in profusion on road-side verges, in meadows and pasture land, and in gardens. It can grow up to about forty or fifty centimetres in the most favourable of circumstances – but usually does not get much more than about thirty centimetres or so. Several different sub-species are described – but they are all best considered as one variety of aster.

The flowers: There is one "flower" to each stem but in common with other asteraceae the flower head is a composite of an outer circumferential array of florets, all yellow in colour, and an inner cluster of florets – again all yellow. Each floret may produce a seed and the seeds are arranged as a white clock as shown in the photograph. The flower heads can be about three to five centimetres in diameter. The flower heads follow the sun – in the morning in summer they face east and in the evening face west – provided the sun is shining. If the day is dull the flowers usually remain closed. I remember picking bunches of dandelion for my mother as a child, always with disappointment, for the flowers just simply closed up and remained closed - thus are useless as brightly coloured house flowers.

The leaves: The long tooth shaped leaves broaden out from a narrow base and give the plant its name – see below. The leaves, the roots and the flower stems exude a white sap when they are broken – this can stain the hands and the areas affected go black temporarily.

The roots: these are "tap roots" and can penetrate the earth very deeply. They can intertwine between other plants' roots and can even push down through narrow cracks in paving.

Names, mythology, uses and folk-lore

There are innumerable local names and Grigson, and the internet, are both a very rich source of them. Just a few are listed here. The French have called it *Dent de Lion (tooth of the lion)* – hence dandelion - and the Germans *Löwenzahn (lions' teeth).* The French have given it another name because of the strong diuretic properties of the leaves – *Pis-en-lit*. As the British schoolboy will tell you this means *piss in the bed*. The leaves, especially when young, have been used in salads and people are advised that if they wish to have a good night's sleep the leaves should not be eaten late! Other names include *fairy clocks, old mans' clocks* or *schoolboy clocks*: the seed heads are said to give the time – blow on the seed head and the number of blows required to remove all the seeds gives the number of hours of the day so far. When the seeds are blown off the remaining part of the seed-head looks a bit like a monk's shaved head and thus the plant has been called *monk's head* in former times. Where-ever the seed lands a new plant is likely to grow provided there is some soil around – even a pavement crack. When growing the plants can crack and penetrate through concrete.

Dandelion has been widely used as a diuretic – a substance that promotes the loss of fluid to the body through the kidneys. Thus it has been used for treating peripheral oedema (dropsy) and for heart failure – this latter use especially in Ireland (Allen and Hatfield). The diuretic properties have been known for many hundreds of years. As mentioned above the leaves can be used in salads – but always choose the younger, small leaves as they tend to be less bitter. Other uses include treatment for warts, for coughs and colds, and innumerable others including lip cancer, scarlet fever, indigestion and corns. It is said that the dried roots make a good substitute for coffee when powdered – but those who have tried it for this tell me that it most certainly is not! The leaves produce ethylene oxide and this can be used to hasten the ripening of recently picked fruit. The dried roots are also used in the preparation of the drink Dandelion and Burdock (q.v. under the lesser burdock description for a recipe).

FEVERFEW

Tanacetum parthenium: *Asteraceae*

The plant: an aromatic plant especially on a warm and still summer evening. It is a downy perennial that grows well in many places including wasteland, grass verges, around walls and on the sides of paths. This was originally a garden plant but is now widely naturalised in the wild.

The flowers: in flower in mid-summer and sometimes later. The flowers have a central disc of quite densely packed yellow florets and an outer layer of white ray florets. Each flower head is about one and a half cm in diameter.

The leaves: quite lengthy and are pinnately divided.

Names, mythology, uses and folk-lore

Some names *include bachelor's button, feather few,* and *stink-daisies*. The leaves from the plant are especially pungent. One of its herbal uses has been to control fevers and to prevent and/or treat migraine and other headaches. Grigson draws a similarity between the plant and modern aspirin.

Pechey describes its value in expelling the afterbirth after delivery of the baby. With camomile it can cure "child-bed purgations in great abundance" – this refers to the vaginal discharge after delivery. Bees dislike it – prevent bee stings by carrying the plant with you. When applied to the top of the head Pechey says it can cure headaches.

Some herbals describe a wide variety of uses and these include treating fevers, irregular periods, arthritis, anaemia, cancer, preventing mis-carriage, bone disorders, swollen feet, diarrhoea, toothache if applied directly to the gums and the common cold. This sounds like a one-stop shop for many of today's common clinical problems and one wonders why the herb is not in more widespread use. One possible reason, of course, is that it does not work.

There is one area where it does work and that is in the prevention of migraine attacks in a proportion of patients suffering from that disease. The Migraine Trust quotes studies which confirm this including a particular study conducted in the year 2005. I have been unable to confirm this.

GOAT'S BEARD

Tragopogon pratensis: *Asteraceae*
(Jack-go-to-bed-at-noon)

The plant: a perennial plant of grassland – although may behave as an annual. It is not especially common although where it is present then many plants may be seen. Grows to about fifty or sixty cm. This was photographed near Rothbury in Northumberland on a grass verge.

The flowers: long bracts open to reveal the yellow florets. Are about two to three cm across. Open only in bright or sunny weather and close up by about mid-day in any case. The flowers give way to the most exotic seed heads which are a shade darker than pure white and about ten cm across – the "goat's beard".

The leaves: are similar to grass and can be difficult to distinguish in grassy places.

Names, mythology, uses and folk-lore

The herbalist Gerard said that this was a garden plant and to the best of his knowledge it grew only in parts of Lancashire. However, he gave a good description of the plant's habit of closing up by noon. It is certainly more widespread now than Gerard perceived it to be. The closing of the flower by noon, or thereabouts, has contributed to some of the colloquial names with which it is associated. These are quoted widely and include *go-to-bed-at-noon, shepherds' clock, one o'clock, sleepy head, twelve o'clock*. Grigson says that another name, *Joseph's flower*, relates to the depiction of Joseph in art which shows him invariably to have a beard. It has also been called St John's flower.

Any medicinal uses that have been attributed to the plant appear to have long since died away. Gerard states that the roots boiled in wine and drunk assuage the pain and pricking stitches of the side. It has also been said that boiling the roots in water and served with butter gave a food that had a good taste, was more delicate than parsnip, and which also strengthened those who have been sick from lingering disease.

GOLDEN ROD

Solidago virgaurea: *Asteraceae*

The plant: Grows to about eighty cm. Seen in a variety of areas – including wooded areas and grassland**.** A perennial plant.

The flowers: Yellow flowers arising in long branching spikes. The flowers have a disc of yellow florets and there are ray florets also. Individual flowers are up to one cm or so in diameter. Flowers from June to September.

The leaves: are narrow except at the base. The lowest ones are also stalked.

Names, mythology, uses and folk-lore

Other names include Aarons's rod a name given also to Agrimony. This refers to an entry in the Old Testament in Numbers 17: v8.

Wikipedia carries a good and well-referenced account of the Golden Rod. This includes a comment that the plant was thought to be of some use in the rubber industry – but this never translated to any product for the rubber from this plant has poor tensile properties.

Gerard knew it as a herb that needed to be imported – and therefore it was held in great esteem by physicians and patients. People, he said, were prepared to pay half a crown for an ounce (roughly twelve and a half pence for thirty g). It was then discovered to be growing in the U.K. – but people seemed unwilling, he said, to spend half a crown on a hundred weight (fifty kilo) of the same plant produced at home. Gerard described no herbal uses but Culpeper did indicating its usefulness in treating external bruises, ruptures, for wound healing and for green wounds, and of ulcers in the mouth, throat and the privy parts of both men and women.

Modern herbals suggest that it has been used as a diuretic, and that it was chewed by native Americans to relieve sore throats (the leaves were used) and toothache – for which the roots were chewed.

CANADIAN GOLDEN ROD

Solidago Canadensis: *Asteraceae*

The plant: grows on damp wayside ground and can reach up to two metres although where I see it in the wild it is usually shorter. Is a garden escapee and frequently seen in areas where it has become naturalised – spreads quite rapidly. In Canada is sometimes rated an invasive plant. It is a perennial and can be quite downy.

The flowers: are very small individually, perhaps only several mm across, but arranged in long sprays and all one-sided and these sprays can branch. Flowers in the later summer – July to October.

The leaves: are lanceolate in appearance.

The golden rod descriptions in older herbals relate to another plant, the solidago virgaurea.

Names, mythology, uses and folk-lore

Various internet sites list modern uses for Goldenrod, but usually Goldenrods seem to be considered as a group. Where the Canadian variety is included in the descriptions there is a recurring theme which links the use of this plant with treatments for pain and swelling, including gout and arthritic pain. Eczema is another condition which seems to feature as being suitable for Goldenrod therapy in one form or another, as is hay-fever, and haemorrhoids, diabetes, tuberculosis, and prostate disease – all claimed to be treatable with Goldenrod. It is also used as a diuretic and is an agent that will treat diarrhoea as well as snakebites. It seems to be administered as a tea for some disorders. Goldenrod is also recommended as an anti-fungal agent.

This selected-out range of uses is very diverse and one wonders why a herb is used when there is a good specific agent to treat each one. The list is reminiscent of some of the various uses applied to plants seen in the old herbals – presented in an era when evidence based medicine did not exist. Although some may disagree my advice is "Do not go there".

GROUNDSEL

Senecio vulgaris: *Asteraceae*

The plant: common plant in a variety of settings. Likes both disturbed grounds and land that is cultivated. Most gardeners will be familiar with the plant! Grows to around fifty or sixty cm and is an annual.

The flowers: these are somewhat cylindrical in outline, about eight to ten mm long and the flower consists of disc florets only. The bracts are green and have black tips. The flowers are yellow and are carried in clusters on the ends of the stems. Groundsel can be seen in flower throughout the year.

The leaves: are lobed and pinnate with the lower ones on stalks. The leaves are soft and are downy on their under-surface.

HEATH GROUNDSEL

Senecio sylvatico: *Asteraceae*

The plant: is a plant of dry ground. Grows to about sixty or seventy cm – is a rather straggly looking plant. In those areas where the plant is evident it will seem very common.

The flowers: are in clusters at the end of the stalks. The flower heads are roughly tubular in shape and quite narrow. The flowers are yellow and consist of only disc florets. The bracts are green. Is in flower only in the summer.

The leaves: are very similar to the groundsel.

Names, mythology, uses and folk-lore

Both plants are considered together in the same way the herbalists seem to have done. *Senecio* is derived from the word *senex* which is a word meaning *downy head*. Also *groundsel* is an old-English name for "pus-absorber".

Other names for the groundsel are *old man in the spring, ground glutton,* and simply *groundsel.* The plant seems to colonise any cultivated garden if it is allowed to, even if there has been no groundsel in sight before. The hairy seeds are able to spread very widely on any breeze.

Culpeper describes it as Venus's mistress-piece and writes "is as gallant and universal medicine for all diseases coming of heat, in what part of the body so ever they be, as the sun shines on". He went on to say that it caused vomiting if the stomach was afflicted and, if the stomach was not affected, purges with more gentleness than can be expected.

In various recipes Culpeper says that it is good against diseases of jaundice, falling sickness (probably epilepsy) and it treats stomach choler (pain). It also "provokes urine and expels gravel". The plant heals liver defects and in poultices will treat the swollen female breast as also with the privy parts of men and women and the seat and fundament (anus). It also treats wounds of the body, sinews and nerves, as well as being useful in appropriate form for treating watering or inflammation of the eyes.

The plants harbour a fungus which can cause disease (rust) in other plants – especially peas, carrots, tomatoes and some ornamental plants.

Lady Wilkinson quotes an old poem describing the groundsel:

Through storm and wind,
Sunshine and shower,
Still will you find
Groundsel in flower.

HAWKWEED
Hieracium species: *Asteraceae*

The plant: The plant can grow to about seventy centimetres, or higher sometimes, and is usually seen in meadows, road-side verges, grassy banks and on woodland paths. Favours drier areas of grassland. Appears in flower in high summer – June to August. The plant pictured here was photographed in June in a meadowland pasture in Northumberland. Where they are seen they are usually very common – but they are absent from many areas: they are best described as being locally common. I have seen a small number of sub-species – the highest estimate of the number is about 17,000 and descriptions that there are over 10,000 varieties of hawkweed are commonly read. Many are not named apparently – so there does appear to be an opportunity for budding botanists who want a PhD degree! It is a perennial. In some parts of the world it has become invasive. Like dandelions the stems have a white exudate when broken (a *bitter-milk* as described by Culpeper).

The flower: Bright yellow and resembles many others in the Aster family when first examined. Each flower head is about three centimetres in diameter, and a number can arise from each hairy stem. However, there is a difference from many asters – for example daisies, in that the flower heads do not consist of two types of florets but only of tightly packed spatulated florets as the picture shows. Each floret has a sharply toothed outer edge. The florets each are attached to the stem through the leafy bracts.

The leaves: these are somewhat ovoid in appearance and, at the base of the plant, arranged in a rosette. Leaves may also arise from the flower stems – these are unstalked.

Names, mythology, uses and folk-lore

Researching local names has been very difficult. There must be many and I would be pleased to hear of any from you. One of the problems is that there do seem to be conflicting names in the herbals and reference books with some dwelling heavily on, for example, mouse-ear hawkweeds (q.v.) or other hawkweed plants.

In terms of uses to which the plant has been applied Culpeper does not let us down. Amongst the huge range of uses described by him are the following: good for the heat of the stomach and for inflammations and the hot fits of agues. The juice of the plant taken in wine helps digestion and hinders crudities left in the stomach. Taken this way also helps the making of water and treats stings from venomous serpents and scorpions. The same benefit is found when a poultice of the plant is applied to the same places. Dried roots taken in wine and vinegar will treat dropsy (fluid retention in heart failure). Taken in various ways Culpeper states that the plant will treat hardness of the spleen, treat coughs and digest phlegm in the chest, procure rest and sleep, hinder "venery" venereous dreams, and restore blood. Applied externally in a woman's milk will treat all diseases of the eyes, and skin ulcers. Distilled water

– presumably from boiling the plants – will cure freckles, spots, "morphew" - which is a skin eruption – and also will cure wrinkles.

Allen and Hatfield suggest that the hawkweeds and mouse-ear have been confused by authors – and that uses attributed to the mouse ear may have been uses attributed to Hieracium.

Studying the hawkweed is not a little confusing. You should be able to recognise some well described hawk-weed like plants from the various wild flower guides but in my opinion finally identifying individual hawkweeds is probably best left to those who have made a special study of the species.

Another plant is the diminutive **mouse-ear**. More recently called a **Hawkweed** but this plant is a Pilosella – **pilosella officinarum**. Seen in dry places and rarely more than about twenty cm tall, it has one flower per stalk and flowers are seen throughout from late Spring to October. The term mouse-ear comes from the leaves which are hairy on top and downy and pale underneath. It has been used to treat throat infections, whooping cough and respiratory infections. Can be quite common.

KNAPWEED

Centaurea nigra (common ~) and centaurea scabiosa (greater ~).

The plant: Two varieties of knapweed are seen. One is the common knapweed and the other the greater knapweed. The common variety is seen more frequently than the greater knapweed, with the latter being found mainly in the southern and eastern parts of England. They grow to sixty to eighty cm in height. The plants are usually seen in grassland, particularly dry grassland, and seem commoner in chalky areas.

The flowers: The flowers of each variety are usually seen between June and September and in appearance the common knapweed appears neater than the greater knapweed, where the outer florets spread outwards laterally, whereas in the common variety the outer florets are more vertically aligned. The flowers are usually solitary at the end of the flowering stem.

The leaves: The leaves on the greater knapweed are basically oblong in shape but are deeply divided. The leaves of the common knapweed tend to be long and narrow.

Names, mythology, uses and folk-lore

Culpeper describes the plant as being owned by Saturn and he gives knapweed a variety of uses. He states that it is good for bleeding in the mouth or nose and other "outward parts" and also it is good for those veins that are "inwardly broken" or bleeding from inward wounds. He indicates that it is good for those bruised by any fall, blows or otherwise and that it is useful in those who have ruptures by drinking the decoction of the roots and herbs in wine and applying the same outwardly to the place.

Culpeper then goes on to list a variety of other uses, including it being singularly good in all running sores, cancerous and fistulous, drying up of the moisture and healing them up so gently without sharpness. He goes on to say that running sores or scabs of the head and other parts can be similarly treated. It aids the healing of all green wounds and has especially been used for the soreness of the throat, swelling of the uvula and jaws, and for staying bleeding.

Grigson does refer to the plant giving it many common names with some of these being applied to the head of the plant - the flower and its hard, somewhat swollen, base. These include *hardheads, hardhack, drumsticks, ironknobs* and *knobweed*. There are many other names quoted by Grigson from different parts of the UK and also Germany. In addition Grigson said that the heads of the plant were being used to foretell the future of love. Unexpanded florets would be picked by girls who then put the heads inside their blouse. If within an hour the unexpanded florets have blossomed this is a sign that love will come their way, soon, from the right person!

Common knapweed is indeed truly common and will be seen on most country walks in the summer time in grassy places. The greater knapweed is best described as being locally common i.e. where it is present many plants are likely to be seen.

LEOPARD'S-BANE

Doronicum pardalianches: *Asteracea*

The plant: almost certainly a garden "escapee" it has successfully become naturalised in the wild. The plant photographed was growing on a shaded railway embankment in the Tyne valley. Sometimes seen in woodlands. It is a perennial and when seen is likely be growing in a drift of plants. The plant grows to about sixty or seventy cm.

The flowers: Are in the typical complex arrangement of the Asteraceae family – a central area of disc florets which are usually just on the orange side of yellow in colour, and outer ray florets which are yellow. The flower is about three cm or a little more in diameter. There is one flower at the end of each stem – but the stems may also be branched with each branch having a terminal flower. It is a flower of early summer.

The leaves: best described as ovoid with the stem leaves being unstalked and appearing to embrace the stem. The lower leaves are stalked.

Names, mythology, uses and folk-lore

Not a lot is written about the plant. Culpeper describes the plant as being a Wolfe's-bane and describes it as being able to strengthen the heart, and as a preservative against pestilence. Culpeper described it as "admirable" against the bites of venomous beasts, and for those who had taken too much opium. It was also described as being useful against "hot rheums" of the eyes.

Gerard does not mention leopard's-bane – but does refer to **wolfe's-bane**. I suspect that the description is unrelated to the Doronicum for the plants he describes, he says, are of the Aconitum family. These plants are highly toxic to man – in Gerard's own words, "deadly".

LESSER BURDOCK

Arctium minus: Asteraceae

The plant: This plant was found by the road-side in the Upper Ingram valley in Northumberland's Cheviot hills. It is virtually identical to the **Greater Burdock** except that it is smaller – less than fifty cm. whilst the greater burdock is usually taller. Although it has the appearance of a shrub the plant is not perennial, but is biennial – germinating in one year and flowering the next. For this reason it does tend to favour waste ground and sometimes disturbed ground as on some roadside verges, but may also be seen in hedgerows and woodland.

The flowers: the flower heads are thistle-like, some fifteen cm or more across. They are on rather spiny-looking bracts and these bracts are hooked, and appear greenish-yellow. The purple florets ***protrude*** beyond these bracts and this characteristic serves to distinguish the lesser burdock from the greater burdock. As the photograph shows the flowers are on spikes with several coming from each stem. The flowers, present from July to September, give way to hooked burs – and therefore beloved by children for sticking on someone else's clothing when thrown at them.

The leaves: these, at the base of the plant, are longer than they are wide – but otherwise are roughly heart shaped and, nearer the top of the plant, they tend to be wider than long.

Dandelion and Burdock is a drink familiar to many: one recipe for this, gleaned from the internet, and untried by me is: cold water – 600ml., 1tsp ground burdock root, 1 tsp of ground dandelion root, 2cm piece of ginger (sliced), one whole star anise (crushed), 1/2 tsp of citric acid, 300g granulated sugar, soda water to taste.

This might bring back childhood memories!

Names, mythology and folk-lore

Most of the herbals refer to the burdocks – but usually lump the greater and lesser together. The internet and also Grigson are both a rich source of names for the plants. These include *buddy weed, clots, clouts* and *clucks* in the north of England, and other names include *wild rhubarb, bachelors' buttons,* and *soldiers' buttons* – this last name coming from the German *Soldatenknöpfer. Flapper jacks, butter-dock, gypsy* or *snake* or *turkey* or *pigs' rhubarb* are among many other names. *Buddy weed* intrigued me but I can find no reason why this name has been used – although researching this on the internet brings up many references to cannabis to which the plant is unrelated.

One name long in use – and still in use – is *sticky jack*: throwing the burs at others usually causes them to stick on clothing.

Herbal uses have included treatments for jaundice, scrofula, inflammatory tumours (could be the same as scrofula – that is tuberculus in aetiology), and flatulence – take internally or apply to the abdomen in a poultice. Also has been used to treat many types of kidney complaints and as a diuretic. Young leaves ingested treat rheumatism and oil from the burdock can be used to treat dandruff. Is sometimes applied to the skin as a "skin tonic" and also has been used as a home remedy to "cleanse the blood". In the early 20th century it was used in parts of the United States to treat "nervousness" by hanging the roots around the neck (of children).

MUGWORT

Artemesia vulgaris: *Asteraceae*

The plant: seen on any disturbed land – often on waste ground or by roadsides. It can grow up to a metre in height. A perennial plant it has become an invasive and troublesome plant in some parts of the world.

The flower: There are innumerable flowering stalks on the plant and each stalk can hold numerous flowers: the flowers are small – about two mm across and five mm in length. Flowers in mid-summer to the early autumn.

The leaves: The upper ones are usually unstalked whilst the lower ones usually are on a stalk. They are each multiply divided and are hairy on their under surface.

Names, mythology, uses and folk-lore

The plant has a variety of colloquial names including *felon herb, wild wormwood, old man, naughty man, sailor's tobacco,* and *mugger.*

The plant has a number of herbal properties. Culpeper said that when applied as a hot decoction to the area would draw down women's courses and aid the delivery of the child and the expulsion of the afterbirth. Made into an ointment with hog's grease it would treat sebaceous cysts ("wens") and it could also cure neck pain especially if a daisy was placed with it.

The herb was good at treating an opium over-dose if the young leaves were chosen. Powder of the plant taken in wine would treat sciatica and a decoction including camomile and agrimony would treat pains of the sinews, and cramps.

The plant has magical properties ascribed to it. Gerard quotes Pliny who said that any traveller wearing mugwort would not be affected by any poisonous medicine, wild beast or the sun, nor would the traveller become wearisome. Its magical properties included being effective against the opium when drunk and, to many other "sorceries" which mentioned God: Gerard refused to list any that dishonoured God – they were, he said, unworthy of recording.

Other magical properties given to the plant included it being able to ward off all the powers of evil, and it would prevent evil spirits and ghosts entering the house.

The plant's potential at treating painful areas is described – roll the leaves up to form a cigarette and then light it and hold the burning end over the affected area (www.happyherbcompany.com/mugwort).

There are also legends linking mugwort to mermaids – a mermaid in Scotland told a lover in Scotland how to treat his lady of consumption.

Churches of the Mediaeval era sometimes show the leaves of the plant carved in to the roof bosses – for example, as in Exeter cathedral (Grigson).

Note: *no magical property should be presumed to be safe or effective. Whilst it is up to the reader to make up her/his own mind my advice is not to experiment with any plant unless you have satisfied yourself that no harm will come from it.*

Upper Teesdale

NIPPLEWORT

Lapsana communis: *Asteraceae*

The plant: a straggly and non-descript plant which it is very easy to walk on by. It grows to about eighty or ninety cm, sometimes more, and is branched. It seems to come up each year in similar places – gardens, disturbed ground, edges of hard-standing such as car parks – but is an annual.

The flowers: often seen in clusters at the top of the plants with each flower being about one and a half cm in diameter. Flowers in July to October. The flower heads are in typical asteraceae fashion with ray florets around the circumference and central disc florets. All are yellow.

The leaves: for the most part these are lanceolate – although some descriptions of the plant say the leaves are oval.

Names, mythology, uses and folk-lore

The name is almost certainly derived from a German origin where it was held in the sixteenth century that the plant *"was good to heal the ulcers of the nipples of women's breasts"*. The flower bud is roughly nipple shaped – hence the name association.

Culpeper says nothing about any uses for the plant but Pechey published that *"Tis reckon'd good for the nipples when they are sore."*

Allen and Hatfield confirm the widespread use of the plant for treating nipple soreness and its use in parts of Ireland for cuts and bruises.

OXEYE DAISY

Leucanthemum vulgare: *Asteraceae*

The plant: The oxeye daisy is a widespread and common plant of summer. It is seen especially in dry grassy meadows, roadside verges and country lanes. It thrives on disturbed soil. It can be quite a tall plant, growing up to fifty or sixty centimetres. It looks, for all the world, like a giant common daisy – but the leaves are different. Equally, at first sight, it can be confused with other asteraceae if only the flowers are examined: it is essential to look for other characteristics as well – for example how many flower heads per stem, branching of the stems, whether hairy or not, and the shape of the leaves. May be covered in a fine hairy down – or the plants can be hairless. It is a perennial.

Flowers: These are solitary – one per stem. They consist of an outer ray of white florets, all of which are sterile, and an inner cluster of tightly packed yellow florets each of which has a stamen and ovary – the fertile part of the plant. The inner florets appear spirally arranged in the flower heads. See Fibonacci rule, pages xv-xvi. Appear in summer from May through to the autumn.

Leaves: The leaves are toothed with those at the base forming a rosette and being somewhat spoon shaped. The leaves which arise from the stem are lobed.

Names, mythology, uses and folk-lore

Oxeye daisy is the correct name for the flower – but I have always known it as *Dog Daisy* and that is how I refer to it when I see it growing. *Dog daisy* is, in fact, an ancient name for the plant. Grigson, always a good source for plant names, gives a large variety of other names including *moon daisy, white gull, rising sun, fried eggs, gowland, gollan* and a legion others. The gowland and gollan names probably refer to daisies. The flower is sometimes associated with St John – one German name is *Johanneskraut (John's plant)* according to Grigson although the Royal Horticultural Society does not mention this in its web-site entry relating to the oxeye daisy. The relationship with St John is seasonal – blooming, as it does, in mid-summer *(solstice flower* and *midsummer daisy* are other names). *Thunder daisy* is yet another name and in parts of Europe, including Germany, it used to be hung on houses and their rooves to protect against thunder lightning strikes.

Culpeper and Gerard appear not to mention the plant in their herbals – but John Pechey, an apothecary in London has offered uses for it. Pechey seems to have been a controversial character of the late seventeenth century – but he said the whole plant, when boiled in posset* drink was an excellent remedy for asthma, consumption (T.B.), and also good for wounds or ulcers when taken inwardly or externally. He also found that drinking a decoction of the herb cured all diseases that are "occasion'd" by drinking cold beer when the body is hot (Grigson). Pechey appeared to have absolute confidence in this plant.

Allen and Hatfield describe its use as a tea for asthma and also for scrofula – TB of the skin. So some of Pechey's claims may have had a sort of foundation to them.

**Posset drink is a precursor of the Syllabub we know today. It was made by boiling up some milk and then decanting it into cold wine – this causing it to curdle.*

PRICKLY SOW THISTLE

Sonchus asper

SMOOTH SOW THISTLE

Sonchus oleraceus: both are *Asteraceae*

The plants: grow to about one m in height. Can behave as an annual or as a biennial. Seen on cultivated land such as gardens, and on waste land. Can become quite invasive and both are common. The plants host aphids and some plant viruses so it is not good to have around.

The flowers: the flower heads are usually seen in clusters reminiscent of umbelliferous plants. Each flower head is about twenty mm in diameter. The arrangement of the flower head is like other asteraceae – there is a central area of disc florets and then an outer layer of ray florets. Flowers in the height of summer from May through to the autumn.

The leaves: the prickly sow thistle has glossy green leaves with a wavy margin which is sharp and has spikes on it to sting or scratch; on the smooth sow thistle the leaves are similarly shaped but are not prickly and are more matte rather than glossy. Breaking the stem of both plants allows a milky sap to exude.

Names, mythology, uses and folk-lore

Both are troublesome invasive plants. Each plant probably has up to eight or nine flowers and each flower produces about 20,000 seeds. So neither are good to have in the garden! Trying to eradicate the plants by pulling them out is only likely to be successful if this is done before any seeds have formed. Several of the States in North America have plans in place to try and eradicate the plants from their jurisdictions. They are regarded as weeds which need control.

Herbalists seem to make no distinction between the various sow thistles. It is said that the leaves make a nutritious vegetable when cooked. This idea appeals to me – you can eat the plant after you have pulled it out of the ground. (However, I have not tried either plant as a food-stuff. I simply pull them out – but even if I do this early in their life-cycle more still seem to grow).

Culpeper has a range of uses for the plants and these include remedies for stomach problems, and for those who are short winded. They have been used to improve lactation in the nursing mother – and, as well, they give a good colour to the nursing baby. One recipe from Culpeper is a "sure remedy" for deafness, he says – *plant juices boiled in a little oil of bitter almonds in the peel of a pomegranate, and then drops placed in to the ear*. I could find no experimental study such as a blind prospective study which has tested this quite specific claim and recipe. The use of an oil may have resulted in ear-wax – a common cause of deafness – being softened and thus come out naturally. Culpeper also recommended that women "in travail" (labour) should make up a recipe of three spoonfuls of the plant juice in white wine and put "thereto" for speeding up delivery.

If women wash using the same fluid recipe their complexion would improve and would have *a good lustre to it!*

SEA ASTER

Aster Tripolium: *Asteraceae*

The plant: A seaside plant, often seen below the upper tide line. Can grow to around sixty cm or so, although those seen by me are always much lower in height.

The flower: This is arranged in a typical aster-like arrangement with lilac coloured ray florets and inner disc florets which are yellow combining to form a single flower head. Often arranged in clusters.

The leaves: These are green, quite thick and fleshy but narrow and elongated.

Names, mythology, uses and folk-lore

Gerard's Herbal describes what I believe to be the sea aster. He calls it *Serapia's Turbith* or *Sea Starwort*. He considers the aster plant under the heading of *Starwort (Starre-wort)*, but he calls the sea aster, if that is what it is, Starre-wort. He describes it as growing along the English coasts in many places and that it flowers in May and June. That is incorrect for it to be a sea aster for the sea aster flowers somewhat later in July and August.

What leads me to believe that Gerard was describing the modern sea aster is that he described that plant as being called tripolium. Gerard describes Dioscorides, stating that a fable attributed to Dioscorides was that the sea aster changes its colour of the flowers three times. In the morning it is white, at noon purple, and in the evening crimson. Gerard seemed to doubt that the flower did change colour and any modern description of the plant does not refer to that apparent fable from Dioscorides.

Gerard describes it being called *blue daisies* or *blue camomile* and in the Harwich area *hogsbeans*. In the edition of Gerard's Herbal which I use, there is no reference to any uses being attributed to the plant, although Grigson states that Gerard recommended the roots of sea aster as a wound herb and also to be used against dropsy and poisons.

Culpeper states that the root of the *turbith* purges phlegm, chiefly from the exterior parts of the body but added "*let not the vulgar be too busy with it*". If *turbith* **is** being referred to by Nicholas Culpeper as the equivalent of the sea aster then it is clear he dismisses the plant. I could find no other herbalist being given over to a description of herbal uses of sea aster. This includes John Pechey's Complete Herbal of Physical Plants, and Allen and Hatfield's book. Even Lady Wilkinson makes no reference to it.

The sea aster photographed here was seen in the higher reaches of the tidal line at Holy Island.

SEA MAYWEED

Tripleurospermum maritimus: *Asteraceae*

(Sometimes known as matricaria maritimus)

The plant: this is a relatively modestly-growing plant which is so obviously a member of the asteraceae family. It rarely exceeds fifty cm in height and is seen most frequently on sandy soil or shingle at about the top of the tide line. The plant is only ever seen on the shore line. It is a perennial. Very similar to scentless mayweed which is an inland plant, although it is altogether rather more untidy in appearance.

The flowers: consist of an outer perimeter of ray florets which are white and central disc florets which are yellow. The flowers are about two to three cm across and have a long flowering season from about Easter-tide to October. This plant was photographed on Holy Island. There is one flower per flowering stem and the base of the stems is sometimes rather purple in colour.

The leaves: these are fleshy and are generally described as segmental and divided many times. Their almost feathery arrangement can be seen in the photograph.

Names, mythology, uses and folk-lore

Many of the chamomile and mayweed plants are very similar. The sea mayweed even has a faint smell of chamomile when the leaves are bruised. In terms of uses and mythology there appears to be nothing written that I could find (this does not mean that it has no mystique relating to it – it simply means I could not find anything). In Iceland the plant is called Baldr's eyelashes. (Baldr is a god of light and purity in Norse mythology, and a son of the god Odin and the goddess Frigg – source Wikipedia. See Lady's bedstraw, pp 18.

SNEEZEWORT

Achilea ptarmica: *Asteraceae*

The plant: A relatively scarce plant but common in those areas where it is seen. This plant was photographed in a very damp moorland ditch in Upper Teesdale – the plant is usually found on acid soils. Can grow to about fifty centimetres or so. It is upright, with sometimes branched stems, and is a perennial.

The flowers: About fifteen mm across for each flower head which is constructed of outer white florets and inner yellowish florets and which form clusters at the top of the plant. Flower stems are hairy.

The leaves: Narrow and arise from the stems without stalks.

Names, mythology, uses and folk-lore

Gerard described the plant and it is thought that this was the first description in the U.K. (sixteenth century). He said the smell caused sneezing *whereof it tooke the name Sternutamentoria – or Neesewort*. In Gerard's time it was mainly a garden plant!

The plant juice, when mixed with vinegar, said Gerard, was good for toothache. The plant is tangy to the taste and chewing it causes salivation. Some names relate to its taste and to its actions – for example *pepper-girse, wild fire, goose tongue, adder's tongue, old man's pepper pot* and the like.

Upper Middlehope Burn in Weardale with old lead mine remnants from 19th century - and a shaft opening.

SPEAR THISTLE

Cirsium vulgare: *Asteraceae*

The plant: a biennial usually living on grassland. Grows to one metre or so in height.

The flower: this is on a spiny bract and each flower consists of many purple florets each a flower in its own right. The thistle flower is between two and three cm in diameter and appear in mid-summer persisting until early autumn.

The leaves: very tough, spiny leaves which are ultimately pinnate in shape.

Names, mythology, uses and folk-lore

The colloquial names listed are not, in my opinion, particularly stunning. These include *bull thistle, Scottish thistle* and *common thistle*.

The stems of the plant have been used as a vegetable when boiled, as have the leaves, but with the prickles removed first. The young leaves are better. This use applies to the other true thistles. The thistle can often be seen to be thriving on grassland – herbivores avoid it.

Grigson discusses why the thistle is the emblem for Scotland – the *Kings of Scotland chose a thistle, not a particular thistle, for its prickliness and the gallant colours. They were not botanists.*

The spear thistle is an "injurious" weed in the U.K. and it is regarded as a noxious weed in Australia and in some parts of the U.S.A.

Culpeper describes carrying about oneself the root of a thistle to cure melancholy (depression). In researching uses for the thistle Allen and Hatfield make the point that many vague descriptions of the thistle in folk literature makes it difficult to be sure as to which species is being used. However, the thistle has been used in treating kidney infections, healing wounds and in the management of tuberculosis.

Pechey describes how a woman with a breast completely destroyed by cancer was "cured" by applying distilled water from the thistle – he called it the Blessed Thistle. He also recommended the thistle for treating scurvy.

Other thistles: there are many species but they often have more a regional distribution rather than being seen everywhere. Those likely to be seen commonly in Northern England and Southern Scotland include: **Spear thistle, Marsh thistle,** the **Creeping thistle** are other varieties photographed here, and the **Melancholy thistle.**

marsh thistle

The welted thistle and the musk thistle are other varieties but these are much less common. It can be very difficult to identify some thistles from one another and a good plant identifying book is best used to assist. Here the spear thistle is photographed before flowering – but the sharp, spear-like leaves are well shown.

Thistles are mentioned in the Bible and when they are there is usually a sin – such as Adam's sin of eating the apple from the tree when Genesis described that God said He would, among other things, bring out thorns and thistles from the earth – Genesis 3:18.

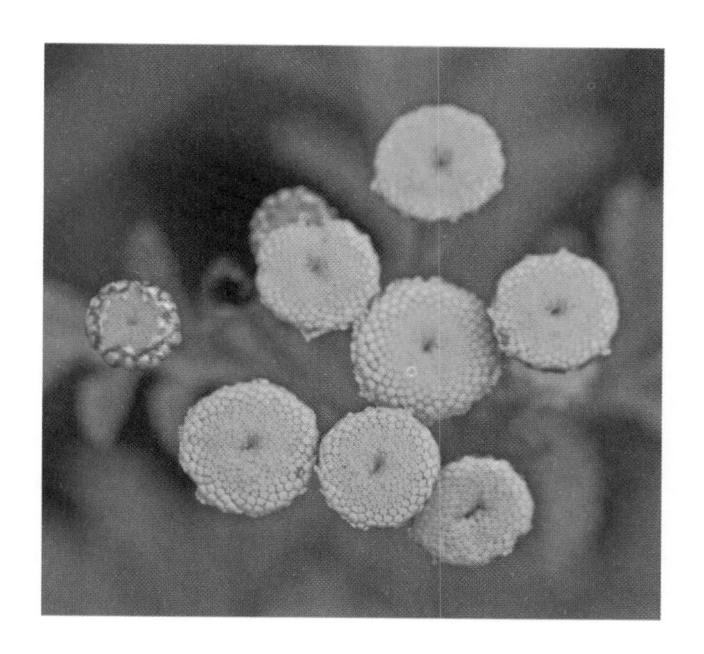

TANSY

Tanacetum vulgare: *Asteraceae*

The plant: An aromatic plant that grows by the roadsides, and on disturbed land. The plant can reach about sixty or seventy cm. Where it occurs it can be quite a proliferative weed, and is a perennial.

The flowers: are for all the world like small buttons. They consist of many florets – but all of them are disc florets – there are no ray florets. Each flower is about seven mm across. The cluster of flowers at the ends of the plants has some of the characteristics of an umbel and these can consist of many flower heads, perhaps up to about sixty or so and the clusters can be upwards of ten to twelve cm across.

The leaves: are like some of the umbelliferous plants with each leaf consisting of leaves which are pinnate in structure and deeply cut lobes.

Names, mythology, uses and folk-lore

The plants are likely all to have had their origins in a garden somewhere – although their escape to the wild could have been some hundreds of years ago. Some of the names include *scented daisies, stinking Willie* and, inevitably, many which include the word *buttons.*

Culpeper has no doubt as to the benefits the wild tansy can confer. He wrote (with reference to wild tansy): Venus hath fitted women with two herbs of one name: the one to help conception, and the other to maintain beauty, and what more can be expected of her. What now remains for you, but to love your husbands, and not be wanting with your poor neighbours? He recommended wearing the herb next to the skin in the shoes – as a result it will stop the terms, if worn so, and the whites too, "for ought I know."

Culpeper also recommended that children who were "bursten" (and by this one suspects that this relates to the abdominal wall and a ventral hernia) and have a rupture could be helped if the herb was boiled in salt and water and then eaten. He said it was good for mouth ulcers, and ulcers in the secret parts, and was very good for inward wounds, and to heal old ulcers and running sores of the legs.

A number of other uses were given for the herb by Culpeper, but already he has given a very wide spectrum clinical efficacy for this plant!

It is a plant seen in modern herbals where, in one, it is recommended for use as a poultice, to treat rheumatism, varicose veins, and bruises – and in homeopathy to expel worms (presumably tape worms). The leaves are claimed to contain an insecticide which can be used to repel flies, ants and fleas, and also mice! This is news to me and when I say that I am suggesting that this use of tansy is probably not widespread in the community. I am sure that most will not be surprised.

YARROW

Achillea millefolium: *Asteraceae*

The plant: a fairly common plant of hedgerows and road side grass verges. Grows to about sixty or seventy cm and its flowering season lasts until very late in the year. It is a perennial and is covered in hairs.

The flowers: are about four or five mm in diameter and are arranged in an umbelliferous pattern. Each flower has an outer ray of several florets, usually about five. These are white or pale pink in colour. There is also a central disc of florets, yellow in colour and about eight in number.

The leaves: dark green in colour and divided into a feathery structure.

Names, mythology, uses and folk-lore

This is an ubiquitous plant and is seen in many countries. Some of its names testify to its international nature: eg. *plumajillo* is the name given to it in New Mexico and Colorado – Spanish for *little feather*. It also has the name *herbal militaris* for it has blood stemming properties (Wikipedia). Other names include *old man's pepper*, *devil's nettle*, *sanguinary* (this name means delighted by, or accompanied by, bloodshed), *soldiers' woundwort*, and *leaf seat*.

The Wikipedia site claims that the fresh leaves can be used to stop nose bleeds, whereas Grigson says that putting the leaves up one's nose stimulates bleeding – he quotes Gerard in saying this!

Culpeper says that an ointment will cure wounds; stop the terms in a woman if a decoction of the herb in white wine is drunk, and will also control the bloody flux. He states that it is good for all green wounds, and also ulcers and fistulae. The shedding of hair can be prevented, he says, if the scalp is bathed with a decoction of the herb. In addition it helps gonorrhoea in men and the whites in women. Leaves chewed in the mouth cure toothache. He adds that it is a very profitable herb for use in cramps and therefore is called militaris.

The reader will go away perplexed that herbalists claim it is good at stopping nose bleeds, and is effective at causing nose bleeds; that it is called militaris because it is good for treating cramps or because it is good for healing wounds. Such happens in non-evidence based recommendations!

SEA THRIFT OR THRIFT

Armeria maritime: *Plumbaginaceae*

The plant: almost exclusively coastal but also seen in salt marshes and there have been occasional reports of the plant being seen on mountains. Rock ledges are commonly colonised by thrift. The plant is also grown in gardens where its beauty is greatly prized.

The flowers: are arranged in densely packed heads of pink florets: the heads are about two cm in diameter and the florets very small. They are seen from spring through to July.

The leaves: usually long and narrow.

Names, mythology, uses, and folk-lore

Names are fairly few and far between. Some names are *pink cushion, Lady's cushion* and *Scawfell Pike*. Another name is *sea grass*. A search on the internet for alternative names yielded a vast range of financial institutions, cut-price stores and also tea rooms.

The plant seems to have been used for centuries as a garden plant for its decorative qualities and its ability to create a cushion-like effect of flowers on the verges and in the rockeries. Perhaps it might be classified as an escapee from the wild.

Gerard says that he has heard of no "Physicke" uses – it was simply a plant esteemed for its beauty.

FIELD SCABIOUS

Knautia arvensis: *Dipsacaceae*

The plant: grows on dry grassland including grassy road verges. It grows to about eighty cm. The specimens photographed here were growing on Holy Island.

The flowers: consist of tightly packed blue-violet florets. If you look carefully you will see that the outer florets, whilst similar to the inner ones, are actually slightly larger. The florets are arranged in an almost dome-like fashion. The flower heads are about three cm in diameter or a little larger and will contain up to fifty or so florets. Flowering season is through summer from June to September.

The leaves: are long and divided.

Names, mythology, uses and folk-lore

Billy buttons, lady's hatpins, pin-cushions and *snake flowers*. There are many other names but many of them including *button* or *cushion*. The scabious plant probably derived its name from its ability seemingly to treat scabies.

Gerard confirms that the plant is a remedy against *"the biles from serpents and stinging venomous beasts – being outwardly applied or taken internally."* One scabious species is described as good for swellings of the upper part of the throat and almonds – given that the treatment was a gargle one presumes that almonds are tonsils.

The plant seems to have had a reputation for treating chest infections for several of the old herbalists describe this. It has also been effective for treating "imposthumes" – abscesses – pleurisy, coughs, quinsy and for diseases of the chest (Pechey). Pechey claims that it could treat the plague. It also cures the itch and little "pocky" ulcers in the fundament (anus) called Rhagades (fissures or cracks).

Culpeper claims that it could treat the French disease – this was syphilis.

Allen and Hatfield state that the plant has been used as a topical treatment for haemorrhoids and, taken internally, for rheumatism. They refer to the devil's bit plant being used against scaly skin (devil's bite).

Memory can play tricks on one – but I feel that the field scabious is now not as commonly seen as used to be the case when it was present, for example, in the cornfields.

Other scabious plants (not shown here) are: ***devil's bit scabious*** (see page xxvi for pict.) – seen more often in the western parts of the U.K. and is recognised as being used for treating bites and scaly skin. It has a flower outwardly similar to the field scabious – but it is a purple colour and not blue. Baker states that one reason the devil's bit got its name was because the devil was envious as to the good it could do and bit away part of the plant.

The other scabious is the ***small scabious***: this plant is seen in England in patches rather than commonly. Although smaller than the other scabious plants, it does grow to about sixty or seventy cm. The flower head is, again, similar, but with the outer florets being obviously larger. The flower head is a pale purple in colour. Probably it has the properties generally attributed to the scabious family in general.

Modern herbals recommend scabious for coughs.

COW PARSLEY

Anthriscus sylvestris: *Apiaceae*

The plant: grows to about one m. in height and is a common sight on road-side verges in the early summer. One of the carrot family of plants, and many of these plants are very similar. They are all characterised by the flowers growing in umbels. Cow parsley is hairy and the stems are hollow. Very difficult to distinguish from ***upright hedge parsley*** (but which flowers later from July to August) and ***rough chervil*** (which has ridged and spotted stems).

The flowers: white, and individually just a mm or two in diameter, in umbels about five or six cm across.

The leaves: are several times pinnate with many arising from each stem. They are green.

Names, mythology, uses and folk-lore

The plant has connections with the devil in folk-lore. Witches used to hang it about themselves. That excellent web site, http://www.plant-lore.com/203/cow-parsley/ describes a number of names associated with the plant, some of which have reminded me of names used by elderly relatives when I was a child. These include *mother-die* and *keks*. Names found in other sites and books include *devil's meat, dead/bad man's oatmeal* and *rabbit meat* (although in my experience that name was usually reserved for dandelions picked for pet rabbits). Cow parsley is sometimes called Queen Anne's lace for it has the appearance of lace similar to that worn by the Queen and her courtiers – however, it shares that 'distinction' with several other carrot family members.

I remember using the hollow stems of this plant as a pea-shooter when I was a young boy!

Its use as a pea-shooter is perhaps the only common use one can find for the plant. However young cow parsley leaves have been added to salads to give an aromatic flavour to the salad mix.

GROUND-ELDER

Aegopodium podagraria: *Apiaceae*

The plant: a perennial that can grow as high as one metre although much less here where it has appeared in a yard where the plant has spread from a garden and underneath the railings. It is hairless and it prefers disturbed ground where it can spread quite rapidly. It is best described as an invasive weed – but, as most gardeners know, when it appears in the garden it is very hard to exterminate.

The flowers: these are white and the umbels in which they appear are up to six cm or so across, as here, and in each umbel there can be a large number of rays, or short stems, - perhaps around fifteen to twenty or so. The flowers appear in June and July usually.

The leaves: are in the shape of an ovoid triangle for the most part, and are in patterns of three.

Names, mythology, uses and folk-lore

Ash weed, Bishop's weed (in Northumberland), *dutch elder, gout weed* and *snow-in-the-mountain* are all given to this plant which was probably introduced in to the British flora; from that introduction it has rapidly spread to be an invasive and troublesome plant. Seen almost anywhere in the U.K.

The time of introduction was probably in the Middle Ages and by the sixteenth century it had become a troublesome weed. The Romans used it as a foodstuff, and the Swedish people have used it in salads and as a pot herb when the leaves are young. At least one can have the satisfaction of helping to control the plant by eating it! If the leaves are picked after flowering the taste is quite pungent, and they can also then provoke a diuresis. This property is not helpful for the leaves are also sedative in action.

Monks used the plant in a medicinal capacity – Hildegaard von Bingen in her practice (details of this appear in *Physica*). I have not yet been able to verify this reference. It is used today where homoeopathy is practised as an agent to treat gout and rheumatism.

PIGNUT

Conopodium majus: *Apiaceae* (sometimes known as Earthnut).

The plant: this is a most delicate plant of woodland areas and sometimes grassy areas also. It grows only to about thirty cm at most. The leaves are most amazingly delicate.

The flowers: are tiny and in umbels of about four or five cm across. Flowering season is April to July although the later times are seen more in the Pennines than in low lying areas. One can walk miles without seeing the plant and then come across areas where it is common.

The leaves: finely delicate leaves, especially at the base, but those further up the plant stems are thin and lobed.

Names, mythology, uses and folk-lore

There are many names for this plant which can be found widely. These include *catnut, scabby hands, lousy arnuts* and *bad man's bread.* Nuts may refer to the fact that the tubers from which the plant grows are, obviously, under the soil surface.

Grigson tells a delightful story when he cites a Victorian botanist saying about the tubers – *they are better fitted to the digestion of respectable quadrupeds with whom it shares its name than for Christian bipeds or those of tender years.* Nevertheless the tubers are sometimes eaten raw – after they have been washed and scraped – there is said to be a crisp and clean taste.

Pechey (1706 in his Compleat herbal of physical plants) describes the nuts being boiled in broth as a pleasant food and one which stimulates *venery* (sexual gratification). When mixed with medicines, said Pechey, it helps those that spit blood or who make a bloody urine.

In Scotland, eating too many pignuts - the tubers – is said to make one's hair full of lice (Grigson).

SANICLE

Sanicula Europa: *Apiaceae*

The plant: lives mainly in woodland areas and, whilst it can be seen in much of the country, it tends to be seen in local areas only. The only site I have seen it is in the grounds of Gibside, a National Trust site in Co. Durham. It is a perennial plant reaching up to about thirty cm, although some references state that it can grow up to fifty cm or so. It is hairless.

The flowers: appear in spring, in May, and can be seen until late summer. They are clustered in small umbels on reddish – pink stems. The flowers are usually tinged with a pink colour although at first sight can appear white.

The leaves: have about five to seven lobes, each of which is toothed. They are hairless, as are the stems.

Names, mythology, uses and folk-lore

A common alternative name is *Butterwort*. Pechey describes it as having significant wound healing properties – it is a vulnerary plant. He said it is active both externally and internally saying that it is useful for treating ulcers and the bloody flux, as well as stopping bleeding.

The recipe he gives for the plant to be effective for bladder ulcers is very complex:

- One and a half drams of the leaves
- One dram of ground pine
- Four scruples of diatragacanth frigid (a mixture of tragacanth and many other plants including melon, water melon, cucumber and gourd seeds)
- Two scruples of sal Prunella (which I do not know at all)

All made up into a powder with a sufficient quantity of lucatellus balsam – then made into a "mass" of pills. Size of pill is not described, but four pills were to be taken twice a day in the morning and the evening.

Another use of sanicle is for starring of the umbilicus when a paste of the plant is applied to the umbilicus and, at the same time, bruised comfrey is applied to the small of the back.

Grigson says that the herb was invoked for the treatment of burns and scalds after the martyr Laurent, later a saint, was griddled to death on a grid iron. The herb was known as *herbe de St Laurent*.

SWEEY CICELY

Myrrhis odorata: *Apiaceae*

The plant: perennial upright plant which can grow to over one m. but which can be somewhat smaller. One of the earliest of the umbelliferous plants to flower. If the stem is bruised it gives off a strong smell of aniseed. Grows best in damp grassland and this plant was photographed in the Northumberland Wildlife Trust reserve at Riding Mill. It is an introduced plant and is widely seen in Northern England and Scotland.

The flowers: in umbels up to five cm in diameter. The individual flowers are tiny and have unequally sized petals and seen in May/early June.

The leaves: the leaves are more like bracken, are up to twenty five cm or so long and are pinnate.

Names, mythology, uses and folk-lore

Names often refer to the aniseed smell – for example *wild anise, annaseed* and *myrrh*. The leaves have resulted in the plant being known as *sweet bracken* in some places, and it has also been known as *sweet humlock (hemlock)* due to its similarity with the hemlock plant.

The plant is used in cookery: it counteracts the acidity of rhubarb if added to that dessert (the leaves are finely chopped and used), and is widely stated to be a good seasoning for stews, soups and salads. Sweet Cicely tea is said to cure indigestion. It can also be infused for a few hours in gin before serving that drink to give a quite distinctive flavour to the "cocktail".

Gerard writes that it grows in "watery ditches" and river sides as well as in meadows. He suggests boiling the flowers in wine and then drinking the brew to make the heart merrie. He said that it far excels all other herbs as a house plant for it "makes the heart merrie and delighteth the senses". It does not cause headaches, says Gerard, "nor does it make meat loathsome as some other sweet smelling herbes do". If the distilled water from the flowers is dropped in to the eyes it takes away the burning and itching, and cleareth the sight.

WILD ANGELICA

Angelica sylvestris: *Apiaceae*

The plant: A tall growing umbelliferous plant which is a perennial. Grows best in damp grassland – but seems almost equally at home in woodland areas. Can reach two and a half metres – but in my experience it is usually shorter. The stems are hollow and have a purple tinge to them**.** It is a most robust plant. **Must not be confused with the hemlock plant which is very similar except the hemlock leaves are much finer. *But take care*!**

The flowers: These are white, usually tinged pink (as if dipped in claret – Grigson) and in umbels, which can appear domed, and up to twelve or so cm in diameter. The individual flowers are very small. Seen June to July, although in the far North they may flower well in August.

The leaves: Each leaf petal is like a pointed ovoid shape and the leaf stem can be quite long – the lowest being up to sixty cm in length. Seem much more robust than many other plants in this family where the leaves can be fern like and delicate.

Names, mythology, uses and folk-lore

There are many names associated with this plant. Some of these include *ground ash, spoots, Holy Ghost, water squirt* (from internet sites and Grigson). The plant also bears some similarities with the hogweed.

Culpeper gives a huge range of uses for the plant which include taking half a dram before breakfast to protect against pestilence and poison and also good for preventing the plague and all epidemic disease. Stalks, candied and eaten, protect against infections, and can warm and comfort the cold stomach, he claimed. Roots steeped in wine and distilled in a glass, taken three times a day, controls "torments" (colic) coming from cold and wind. In various preparations the herb treats pleurisy, breast disease and shortness of breath. Dropped in to eyes aids dimness of sight, and eases the pain "of hollow teeth".

Seems to be largely ignored by herbalists today but most of the carrot family is edible – again, beware the hemlock! Wild angelica has certainly been used in modern times as a foodstuff.

The garden variety has been used, and probably still is, by putting candy on to the young stems and then selling the products as sweets, or as cake decoration.

In some countries wild angelica has been identified as an invasive species which requires careful management to combat the risk that it might take over areas and thus prevent other species of wild flower to grow.

RED VALERIAN

Centranthus ruber: *Valerianaceae*

The plant: A perennial plant growing to about eighty cm in height. It seems to thrive best on poor soils – even on rocky soil and can grow from crevices in old walls.

The flowers: are pinkish-red and the small flowers are arranged in dense clusters at the end of stalks. Each flower is about eight mm long. Some of the flowers can be white. Appear in flower from May until the early autumn.

The leaves: these are in opposite pairs on the stems. Are green.

Names, mythology, uses and folk-lore

Some of the names are *setwall, capon's tail* and *bloody butcher*. There are several valerian types – **marsh** and **common** varieties being the others to note: these usually have white/pink flowers. Where one plant is found there will usually be several others nearby. The red valerian is an introduced plant but is now very widely naturalised in the wild. The leaves of the common valerian have been used as a tea.

The red variety probably first escaped from gardens in the mediaeval period – before the 15th century. Gerard describes uses for the valerian as a group: the dried roots were useful in mixtures against poisons, and the plants were put into broths and stews – and also physical meats. Gerard described this happening amongst the poor of our northern parts. He quotes "some woman poet or other" who wrote:

They that will have their heale
Must put setwall in their keale.

Other uses for valerian have included, as a common theme in various writings, aiding wound healing. Modern herbals also refer to its value in treating "nervous disorders" and in acting as a sedative. Only the roots are used for this.

The leaves are bitter but young ones can have this reduced by boiling and then they can be used as a spinach-like vegetable.

BIBLIOGRAPHY

Some of the following have been used in preparing this book and a number of others are also referenced. They are all good reads!

Current books

Allen and Hatfield: Medicinal Plants in Folk Tradition. Pub: Timber Press, Cambridge, 2004. This book is in print and available to purchase. It is a good reference work. A discussion has been held with Timber Press regarding reproduction rights as I have just not been able to contact the authors. The quotations are given under the "fair use" arrangement – as I would do if preparing a scientific paper. ***I strongly recommend this book to anyone interested in Folk Medicines. It is well researched and well referenced – and a good read.***

Margaret Baker: Discovering the Folk-lore of Plants. Pub: Shire Publications Ltd., 2011. A lovely book and gives a good background read to many plants. Illustrations are line drawings.

Ian Burrows: Food from the Wild. Pub: New Holland Publishers, London 2005 This book is referred to only occasionally – it was used only two or three times to give a culinary reference point in the text. I cannot comment on the book's usefulness in general for those searching food from the wild, but I have found it to be as good as any book in this category for background reading.

David Lang: Orchids of Britain. Pub Oxford University Press 1980. Currently a new edition available called Britain's Orchids, and published in 2004. The 1980 book is quoted once only in the text – but it is an interesting guide to that most difficult group of plants, wild orchids. The photographs of the 1980 edition are not always easy to interpret but David Lang's books are great to read and learn about the complicated lives of some of Britain's most glamorous plants.

Richard Maybey: Flora Britannica. Pub: Chatto and Windus, London. Although only one or two quotations are made this is an encyclopaedic book on wild flowers written in a very easy and relaxing style. Certainly worthwhile obtaining a copy.

Richard Maybey: Weeds. Pub: Profile Books Ltd, London, 2010 A book that can be read from cover to cover without any problems. It is more than a dip in and dip out book – it is one that encourages reading. A fascinating account of weeds!

Roger Phillips: Herbs and Medicinal Plants. Pub: Elm Tree Books, London 1987. **Dietrich Podlech: Herbs and Healing Plants of Britain & Europe.**_Pub: HarperCollins Publishers Ltd, 2008. These two books are good background reading. I am not a herbalist, nor do I recommend herbal treatments in general, but these books do assist in discovering current usage of many herbs. They are easy to read.

Paul Sterry: Collins Complete Guide to British Wildflowers. Pub: HarperCollins Publishers Ltd, London. This book is in print and is widely available. Very good book: just about light enough to carry around on a country walk. The photographs for the main part are clear although are relatively small. In my view easily the best available book on plant identification.

Nan Sykes: Picture Guide to the Wild Flowers of North East Yorkshire. Pub: North York Moors National Park Authority. A more regional book – but again an excellent plant identifier.

Older books

Nicholas Culpeper: Culpeper's Complete Herbal. Facsimile from Lightning Press Ltd (available on Amazon). No one interested in the herbal history of medicine should be without it.

John Gerard: Historie of Plants (Gerard's Herbal). Pub: Tiger Books International Ltd. The edition I have used is an edition edited by Marcus Woodward 1927 (a very much abbreviated version of Gerard's main work). An early and authoritative work – recommended.

Geoffrey Grigson: The Englishman's Flora. Pub: Phoenix House Ltd 1958 This book occasionally appears on Amazon and elsewhere as a second-hand book: if you see it advertised grab it while you can. It is a superb reference book. Sadly Geoffrey Grigson died about thirty years ago and the publishers appear no longer to be in business, but every attempt has been made to contact them.

John Pechey: The complete herbal of physical plants: First published 1707 and facsimile available from Eighteenth Century Collection Online Print Edition. A remarkable book with much detail in it of recipes for herbal treatments.

John Wallis: The natural history and antiquities of Northumberland and so much of the county of Durham as lies between the Rivers of Tyne and Tweed; commonly called North Bishoprick. Vol 1; Pub: HardPress Publishing, Miami, Florida. This is a facsimile of a book by the Revd John Wallis A.M. It is a good read – but there is no plant index so finding plants is not easy. The section containing the wild flowers is detailed – especially to where precisely in Northumberland the plants may be found. Originally published in 1769.

Other sources: the internet is a very rich resource although I have found when researching a plant that one may need to go to many sites to get the fullest information. Some web-sites are better than others, and one sometimes discovers that many entries under a plant's name results in restaurants, laundries and various other establishments appearing in the lists produced by the search engine. Sometimes contrary information is presented and that can be a worry – which is correct? However the following I have found helpful and list them here but not in order of preference – although the first named is the most useful one for my needs in preparing this book – and permission has been granted for the quotations I have made from it to be published here. The web-site is: www.plant-lore.com

Various other sites which I have found to be useful and reliable include:

www.wildlifetrusts.org/

www.botanical.com/

http://www.british-wild-flowers.co.uk/

www.ukwildflowers.com/

Other sites are referenced in the text. Because of my innate suspicion of websites I have always sought a second reference to the flower, comments, folk-lore etc. that may have been revealed. As far as I can tell the web-sites I give here are first rate although I must confess that any information I have used has been usually of a more general nature.

Please note: readers might like to visit gardens in the area. The first to mention is **Alnwick Garden**. This famous garden is open most of the year – may have a closure in January for maintenance work – but opening times can be checked at www.alnwickgarden.com. Another garden to visit is the **Dilston Physic Garden**, nr. Corbridge. The opening times are more limited than Alnwick – Wednesday and Saturday from May to September. Visit the site on www.dilstonphysicgarden.com for opening times and directions to the site.

GLOSSARY OF TERMS

The following words crop up regularly in the old herbal literature and I give the meaning of these here. There are one or two names for which I can only give (hopefully) an intelligent guess:

Agues – a condition with intermittent fevers, usually associated with malaria

Annual – a plant that grows from seed and completes its life cycle each year

Aphrodisiac – a substance increasing sexual desire

Arbortifacient – substance causing abortion

Argema – Greek word for eye disorders

Asthma – an allergic response which is associated with wheezing and difficulty in both breathing in as well as out

Biennial – a plant that germinates in one year and flowers the next, then produces its seed and dies off

Bloody flux – dysentery

Broth – water based food somewhere between a thick stew and soup

Cankers –mouth ulcers often of the aphthous type

Choler – one of the four "bodily humours" associated with bile and usually meaning an irritable or angry persona

Choleric – bad-tempered, irritable, intolerant and many other similar descriptions

Claver – clover

Cod – seed pod

Colic – abdominal pain usually arising from the gut or the renal tract to overcome an obstruction in the lumen. Pressure increases in the gut as the contractions become greater to try and overcome the obstruction with the production of increasingly severe pain: this is usually followed by a short period of relative ease before the cycle is repeated ever more severely. Bowel tumours, constipation, gall stones, renal stones are probably the commonest cause

Decoction – of extracting active ingredients from a substance, ie a plant, which may be any part of it from roots to flower. Plant is mashed and boiled in water for eight to ten minutes usually

Defluction – a word now no longer used but meaning running eyes due to colds, 'flu and the like

Digestive – relating to digestion and possibly referring to the stomach

Diuretic – something that increases the rate at which the kidney excretes fluid

Falling sickness – probably epilepsy

Fistula – literally a communication tube between two surfaces lined with epithelium. Common in those times of Culpeper, Gerard and others. Examples would include gut to skin in which, for example, an area of infection associated with the gut discharges through the skin – the fistulous tube arises where the abscess had been and it persists. Bladder to gut fistulae were common and very often they would be associated with tuberculosis or Crohn's disease although it would probably be called tuberculosis at that time

Floret – literally a tiny flower, often used to call the small disc flowers seen in asteraceae plants

Flux – usually refers to bloody diarrhoea due to a number of pathogenic gut organisms including dysentery

French disease – syphilis, a sexually transmitted disease without any treatment possible until penicillin arrived on the scene. Chronic illness with sufferers having a variety of late complications, twenty or more years after the primary infection - including aneurysms (swelling with associated weakness of a vessel wall and risk of spontaneous rupture) of arteries, insanity, loss of peripheral neurological sensations and paralysis. Late stage syphilis rarely seen today – but not totally absent!

Fundament – buttocks, anus

Gonorrhoea – a sexually transmitted disease now treatable by penicillin, but prior to antibiotics very difficult to treat

Gollan – daisy like. Sometimes associated with yellow flowers.

Gowk – cuckoo

Green sickness – iron deficiency anaemia of young women

Green wounds –usually a long-standing wound and even now difficult to treat other than surgical excision of the affected tissue

Gripings – usually recurring stomach pains

Halitosis – bad breath often from poor oral hygiene

Hermaphrodite – a plant or animal having both male and female functioning sex organs

Hot rheums – hot-feeling discharge from the eyes or bowel

Humours – governing principles in bodily health with astrological associations (Culpeper)

Hybridisation – combining a new organism or plant by cross breeding from two separate parent species. The first generation of that in plants is known as the *F1 hybrid*.

Imposthumes – pus-filled abscesses

Kernels – a small solid swelling probably

Injurious weed – A weed officially designated as injurious to habitat, ecosystem, agriculture, humans or animals

King's evil – scrofula or tuberculosis of the skin (very common incurable disease in past times). Tuberculosis is still a common world disease affecting the lungs especially but also many other tissues including the skin

Knots – uncertain origin but may relate to muscle knots

Ladies'/women's courses – menstruation, which many ladies centuries ago, as today, tried to disguise

Lasks – diarrhoea and/or flux (see above)

Morphew – scurfy skin eruption

Parasitic worms – usually tapeworms living in the gut. Still very common in many parts of the world and diseases occur as a result including malnutrition

Perennial – a plant that grows every year from the same rootstock

Pestilence – a disease which usually causes death ie the plague. Some associate pestilence with one of the four horsemen of the Apocalypse symbolising the plague, or a contagious disease, and which reflects an interpretation of the book of Revelation in the Bible.

Phlegmatic humours – probably a temperate, serene person

Phthisic – relating to chronic lung disease – usually tuberculosis. Spes phthisica is a term used in previous eras to describe the euphoria sometimes seen in patients with (usually) advanced tuberculosis

Physick – a medicine

Piles – haemorrhoids

Pint eg *cuckoo pint* – short for pintle an old English term for penis

Plague – a disease spread by ticks from rats and very common in Europe until cleaner water and better sanitary conditions were achieved. The infecting organism is Yersinia pestis. It is still endemic in many parts of the world and is a very serious condition, and was usually fatal in the Great Plague of the 17th century – Culpeper was much involved in the control of that disease. The nursery rhyme of Ring-a-ring of roses is associated with the plague: if the person thought they could smell roses and then began sneezing were usually cut down by the disease.

Possets – hot drink of milk curdled with wine or beer

Quinsy – a peritonsillar abscess: can be a very dangerous condition of the throat

Rabid – mad dogs suffering from rabies

Scrofula – tuberculosis of the skin

St Anthony's Fire – a disease caused by ergot poisoning from a common wheat fungus especially in the more central parts of Europe, but sometime people say incorrectly that it is due to an infection called erysipelas due to a bacterial organism, or a moderately severe attack of herpes. Ergot poisoning variety was very severe and would cause madness, hallucinations, patients' bodies and limbs would be writhing with severe burning pains in the legs when in bed and sufferers used to run wildly in the streets, and they vomited

Terms (in women) – probably related to the menstrual cycle

Tertian – a condition with relapsing fever, eg. Malaria

Tertian ague – probably relates to the fever of malaria

Toxic – poisonous

Vulnerary – a herb associated with wound healing

Wen – sebaceous cyst: in mediaeval times could become very large but now usually removed before this happens (but not always)

Whites in women - probably relating to a thrush infection but I am uncertain

Wort – a plant or herb associated with healing

SOME OLD MEASURES

Volume:

Unit	Imp ounce	Imp pint	Millilitres	Cubic inches
Fluid ounce	1	1/20	28.4	1.73
Gill	5	¼	142.1	8.67
Pint	20	1	568.3	34.7
Quart	40	2	1,136.5	69.4
Gallon	160	8	4,546	277.4

Imp is short for Imperial. U.S. ounces and pints are different in size – slightly smaller!

Mass:

Unit	Pounds	Grams	Kilo
Grain	1/7000	0.064	
Drachm	1/256	1.78	
Ounce	1/16	28.35	
Pound	1	453.6	0.454
Stone	14	6,350.3	6.35
Quarter	28		12.7
Hundredweight	112		50.8
Ton	2240		1,016

British apothecaries' volume units

Unit	Symbols and abbreviations	Relative to previous	Metric value
Minim	1 ♏		59.1μl
Fluid scruple	fl℈	20 minims	1.18ml
Fluid drachm	flʒ	3 fluid scruples	3.55ml
Fluid ounce	fl℥	8 fluid drachms	28.41ml
Pint	O, pt	20 fluid ounces	568.3ml
Gallon	C, gal	8 pints	4.55l

Top row is one minim, the next three are prefaced symbols with fl – fluid. The symbols were often used on prescriptions particularly before the 1950's although their usage did linger with older doctors for a while.

INDEX